DOMENIC ZARRELLA

SANITY

IT'S OPTIONAL IN TODAY'S CULTURE

THE ONLY THING STRONGER THAN FEAR IS FAITH

Extreme Overflow Publishing
Dacula, GA
USA

Extreme Overflow Publishing
Dacula, GA
USA

Extreme Overflow Publishing
A Brand of Extreme Overflow Enterprises, Inc
P.O. Box 1811
Dacula, GA 30019
www.extremeoverflow.com

Send feedback to info@extremeoverflow.com

Photo by *Angelica Studios*

Printed in the United States of America
Library of Congress Catalogin-Publication
Data is available for this title. ISBN: 978-1-7379262-5-2

DOMENIC ZARRELLA
SANITY
THE ONLY THING STRONGER THAN FEAR IS FAITH

DEDICATION

To my father, Alfred Orlando Zarrella, Sr., who passed away on January 17, 2019, at 90, from prostate cancer and old age.

Papa taught me how to be a father, the best thing that I am. After all the vocations and directions that I've pursued in life, I found my calling in being a father, and all the skills necessary to be the father of a family: provider, protector, and leader of the family to Faith in God. But mostly what's needed to be a father is lots of love for his wife and kids, a loving wife who is an exemplary mother, extended family, outside role models to help form the kids, upright friends to make life twice as good in the happy times, and half as bad in the tough times. Pastors and other strong men in the religious life. And a little help from the Father of all Fathers, God Himself.

To my mother, Florence Marie Zarrella, who passed away October 18, 2019, at 87, from heart complications and a broken heart (my father passed away nine months prior). She gave me my big heart, openness to other people, and my strong Faith through dedication to our Blessed Mother. Her "Hail Mary" prayer during my first nervous breakdown was the inflection point between my drifting from the Catholic Church to returning to the forgiving and merciful heart of Our Father in Heaven.

I hope you're proud of me, Mom!

To my kids, Bianca, Dominique, Zachary, and Giavanna. You can't be a great father without kids who are willing to listen, learn, and follow. They stepped up to help me the last 12 months as they became young adults themselves and returned the goodness that I had given them growing up. Great buffers between my wife, Dee, and me when times got tough in the last few months. My intent on writing this book is to somehow explain the internal aspects of what they witnessed externally.

I'm proud of you!

TABLE OF CONTENTS

ACKNOWLEGEMENTS

To Tricia Fitzgerald from the NAMI Peer-to-Peer class. For taking the time to read my book, being only the second person to read the first draft after my sister Angela. And for encouraging me when I was uncertain that it was a story that people wanted to hear. I hope you write your own book soon!

To Deborah Mitchell, Evangelist and author of "Poppin Beans," a book encouraging Faith and Family Traditions. Thank you for connecting me with Extreme Overflow Publishing!

To Yolanda Lewis, my Publisher, Sarah Banick, my editor, and Karen Penn, cover designer, For having the same vision for this book as I did.

INTRODUCTION

Does sanity exist anymore? In today's culture, is it optional? If so, is it used to your advantage or disadvantage?

These are the questions I ask, sitting on the Lancaster, Massachusetts town beach on Spec Pond. Given the state of the world today—with divorce and broken families, the addiction and suicide rates, rampant crime and mass shootings, depression/anxiety and other mental illnesses, political and employment uncertainty, computer viruses and the coronavirus, racial inequality and civil unrest, wars and asymmetrical wars, and the list goes on—are we really living in a sane society? Have we gotten so used to it that we don't notice anymore?

Statistics show that anyone reading this book may be close to someone with a serious mental illness (59 percent of people, according to a Harris Poll conducted by the American Psychological Association). This includes bipolar disorder, schizophrenia, major depression, anxiety, psychosis, PTSD, ADHD, Asperger's, and all the other new diagnoses. Have you ever wondered what was going on inside the mind of a loved one with mental illness when they did all those crazy things? This book is an attempt to answer that question for my children, especially my two oldest daughters who walked with me through two Psychiatric hospitalizations, as well as any other supportive family member who wants to support their loved one's wellness journey.

Having been privileged enough to live a middle-class or upper-middle-class life, I've been blessed. But the rapid changes in our society, and the technological advances driving them, have been spectacular. We're encouraged to embrace change, think more positively, and multitask like our lives depend on it – and in many ways our careers do. Is there any time to stop and think? Or to take a vacation without bringing your laptop? I question whether our modern lifestyle is advancing mankind or setting it back into an unknown wasteland. My observation is that it's a very fast-paced, hustle-and-bustle treadmill that you never really advance on.

Can you stand to see another emotional bully rule the day in corporate America or any other sphere of our society today? What are we doing to ourselves? Why? Is anyone even sane enough to ask the questions?

The news isn't all bad. There are still many compassionate people in our society, very many. They're willing to work and suffer with our youth, our mentally ill, our addicted, and our elderly. Teachers, doctors, counselors, co-workers, neighbors, family, and friends all have a place in supporting the return of sanity to our society.

Is anyone willing to try God for a change? Or are we afraid he will let us down like some of our religious leaders have? Even if you consider yourself the most unforgivable sinner, His infinite mercy is open to us all. After all, we're all sinners, and the greatest sinners became the greatest saints.

This book looks at modern-day life through the eyes of, arguably, one of the successful travelers in the American mental health system. It's the best mental health system in the world, but in a country where it's most urgently needed. It's a religious book, written by a Catholic, but many manic/psychotic episodes are religious or spiritual in nature. Catholic means universal, so it may captivate anyone. It's a non-fiction book, but could be considered fiction if you have trouble believing the ramblings of the manic/psychotic individual who wrote it. I let you into the mind of someone who has emerged from insanity intact.

CHAPTER 1

A WILD RIDE TO SANITY

"Dad, everyone is concerned about you. Will you meet me and Bianca at the Mass General (hospital) emergency room today?**"**

My 24-year-old daughter, Dominique, called me on my cell phone on Super Bowl Sunday, February 3, 2019—the day the Patriots were playing the Rams in Super Bowl LIII.

I had other plans for that afternoon, as you can imagine, but I agreed to meet my two oldest daughters at 3 p.m. to assure them that I was OK. At 57, married 28 years with four children (including Zach and Gigi also), an electrical engineer selling high-tech semiconductors for most of my career, I was in a manic/psychotic state that only my wife, Dee, could recognize. Well, maybe a few others had noticed.

We watched the Super Bowl in the emergency room of Mass General as the doctors were arranging a bed for me in the psychiatric ward of another hospital. Bianca and Dominique, who were both working at Mass General on gap-years before medical school, were good company during these hours of uncertainty. We waited 24 hours in the emergency room with other severely ill patients, some of whom were violent. So began a humbling 12-day stay at McLean Hospital in Belmont for bipolar disorder with psychotic features, followed by a six-day partial program at Marlborough Hospital.

Even in the state of mind that I was in, I knew many, many mentally ill people who weren't as fortunate as I was in getting the proper treatment. Without health insurance, or at least not of the quality that I had, and no family to guide them through the maze of the mental health system, many people that I had come across since being diagnosed in 1995 floundered through life.

Still, the treatment that we get today is magnitudes greater than when my Aunt Josie and others in my family were treated a generation ago—I don't know how they did it because the mental anguish I've suffered has been excruciating enough. Diagnosed with bipolar disorder with psychotic features (a thought disorder) in 1995 during an emergency room visit after a short ambulance ride, I had no idea that bipolar ran in my family. I probably wasn't told due to the stigma of mental illness in those days, or because my parents didn't want to scare us kids. I was hospitalized again in 1998 and 1999 while trying different med combinations: mood stabilizers and anti-psychotics.

Chapter 1

From 1995 until the Great Recession in 2009, I managed to have a successful-enough career to allow my wife Dee to stay home with the kids. Of course, I had access to the best doctors for meds and counseling.

But this time I had gone off my meds—twice! Once in September, resulting in hospitalization at Newton-Wellesley Hospital, and this time. No, I don't recommend getting off your meds, and I hadn't done it in 24 years of treatment, but I felt that I was in a lose-lose situation in another high-stress, high-tech sales job that I didn't have the capacity to perform in. Although I had the latest miracle drugs, side-effects like mental fog, cognitive and memory losses, fatigue, and the fast pace of business today, I couldn't compete. I went off my meds out of desperation.

Fast-forward to today, and my teams at Newton-Wellesley, McLean, and Marlborough introduced me to the latest meds with fewer side effects—my head is much clearer. Counseling taught me a new way to look at other people's point-of-views, and the needs that they're trying to meet (albeit sometimes done in aggressive or negative ways) and how to respond to them better. I was also able to semi-retire, substitute teaching K-12 part-time and collecting Social Security Disability in order to reduce the stresses that compound bipolar disorder. I'm at peace.

If only it hadn't taken 24 years to accomplish, my recovery would have saved a lot anguish on the part of myself, my wife, and my family, friends, and co-workers. I realize that the times and treatments were different in 1995, but now we have the opportunity to diagnose, treat, and follow up with the unfortunate individuals who, many times through no fault of their own, are gripped by genetic or situational mental illness.

CHAPTER 2

THE (MANIC) EPISODE BEGINS

Domenic, what are you going to do now?" asked my prescribing nurse practitioner, Pat Senior, in her office at Island Counseling in Worcester in the late fall of 2017, 18 months before my episode at Mass General. I had just been laid off for the third time since the Great Recession of 2009 when the demand for semiconductor "chips" departed from the Northeast market. The weight of my Bipolar and medicine side-effects didn't increase my chances of being the best-of-the-best who would remain employed. It was difficult to find and hold a job.

"I'm going to do what I've always done, search for a job," I responded. The expression on Pat's face wasn't very encouraging. "You look too medicated to be interviewing," she shot back. Pat always gave me two options when my treatment reached a crossroad, which empowered me. "We either reduce your lithium slightly, maintaining the Risperdal where it is, or you go back on Social Security Disability (SSDI) and work part-time again."

I always loved Pat's practical approach. I had been accepted on SSDI in 2011 after my two years of unemployment ran out – remember that they had extended unemployment to two years in the Great Recession. Having made over the maximum salary paying into SSDI for many years, I got the maximum benefit when SSDI declared me disabled after a close brush with ECT (shock treatment) that my psychiatrist, Dr. Michael Isaiah Bennett, ultimately recommended that I decline. The hospital that evaluated me recommended it. I had never been so depressed in my life! But I wasn't suicidal, and Dr. Bennett said the depression would lift eventually. In the end he was right, it did. Disability wasn't much compared to my earnings potential, but it did pay the mortgage on our dream home in Leominster, Massachusetts, an hour outside of Boston. I bet our neighbors in our upper-middle class neighborhood appreciated the fact that the unemployment extension and SSDI might have saved our house from foreclosure! I certainly did. Dee had returned to work in a professional career after getting an MBA while being home with the kids since 1994, providing the brunt of support for the family now.

From 2011 to 2018, I went back to work on SSDI trial periods three times and failed every time.

I chose Pat's option #1, and we started our attack on the job market right away, reducing the lithium slightly but still in the range of the quarterly blood test for lithium levels. It was a risky approach because while I couldn't be too medicated in order to perform crisply in the fast-paced, high stress environment of semiconductor sales, the more stress I was under when working in this environment, the higher the dose of meds I needed. Catch-22.

Dee was accepting of this plan because she always believed in my ability to combine the brains I used to obtain a "Double E" (bachelor's degree in electrical engineering) with the social skills required in sales. Sometimes I questioned whether Dee had too much confidence in me, as I considered retreating back into a component engineering position on the technical purchasing side of the sales transaction, where I had been until October 1994 before entering sales. But I loved the work of assisting the designers of cell phones, computer servers, networking routers, computer storage and graphics, military and defense equipment – and everything else an electronics hardware company in the U.S. could dream up. I was employed by Hyundai Electronics, Samsung Semiconductor, and PLX Technologies during the height of my sales career of 15 years. And we were literally splitting nanoseconds in this work. A nanosecond is one-billionth of a second, $1 \times 10(-9)$ seconds. Putting four gigabits on a single semiconductor memory "chip." A gigabit is a billion bits. Each bit has one transistor, and a bit is a binary "1" or a "0." We were running these "chips" at one gigabit per second. When your cell phone carrier says their network runs at one gig, they mean that it transmits 1 gigabit (billion bits) per second. No wonder that when you Google information today, it downloads almost instantaneously.

So I polished off my resume and started the job search. Always skilled at career networking and interviewing, I had some good prospects. This was the winter of 2017, and in the spring of 2018, I got a call from my old friend and co-worker from Hyundai, Dana Peters. He was searching for a regional sales manager for the company he worked for, ACC, a maker of capacitors, near Newport, Rhode Island. Dana is the epidemy of a salesman: sharp, witty, and smart. Dana loved putting technology deals together between people and companies. He knew about my bipolar disorder and was willing to take a risk – he was always willing to take a calculated risk if a good reward was involved. Matched with my conservative approach, we made a good team. On top of that, Dana and my boss at Hyundai, Ken Heller, rode the rocky road of my early years with bipolar, from 1996 to 2001.

I got the job at ACC and started working there June 4, 2018, the day before my youngest daughter, Giavanna, turned 18. In the interview, I was honest with the CEO and owner of the company, Dana's boss Jim Haley, about my bipolar diagnosis. I had become more and more accustomed to sharing my diagnosis with employers, coworkers, family, and friends since society had become more open to mental illness in the time between 1995 and now; but when meeting new people, I didn't lead with it, if it wasn't important that they knew.

And this is where I let you into the mind of one particular character in the world of mental illness, me! Just before Christmas of 2017, six months prior to starting at ACC, my buddy from high school and best man, Mario, was rushed to UMass hospital in Worcester for quintuple bypass surgery. Not outrageously unusual for a 57-year-old man, and I visited him often since I was out of work. He recovered quickly, but on May 3, a month before I started working for ACC, my other close friend, Huck, had a heart attack and bypass surgery. He was also lucky enough to be treated at UMass Worcester. This is where it gets interesting, so pay close attention: A psychotic thinking disorder called "ideas of reference" caused me to believe that I was responsible for Mario and Huck's heart problems. I knew that these intrusive thoughts were unfounded, and since I had experience with them before when I was ill, I didn't believe them.

However, unlike when a normal person listens to music in the background at a doctor's office but doesn't really hear it, these thoughts were more than in the background – they were up front and center! I struggled with them only briefly before increasing my Risperdal anti-psychotic and calling Pat Senior's office to make an appointment, but due to the disarray of my thinking, I wasn't positive that I could make it to the appointment. So I checked into the UMass Worcester Emergency Room on May 4, 2018, the day after Huck was admitted to the same hospital.

I was evaluated for the usual physical indicators, waited, then waited more, before being asked if I wanted to enter the psych ward for further evaluation. I was determined to take this as far as it needed to go, even if it meant being admitted – which is the scariest decision that a mentally ill person must make or have made for them. But I also knew that I had caught this early in the process, which increased my odds of rebounding quickly and missing the pleasure of having my shoelaces and belt confiscated and being admitted. So I met with the psychiatrist and explained the situation – I was good at that, very clear, not my first rodeo. I remember her saying, "Domenic, I understand that you're not feeling well and that you're scared, but I have nine other people ahead of you that are much more serious than you. If you'd like to wait for further evaluation, fine. But alternatively, if you're okay with it, you could continue to take the increased Risperdal, and we'll get you an appointment with Pat Senior ASAP." That was all I needed to hear before choosing the latter option—going home and continuing my treatment outpatient.

It's a relief when you put your situation into the hands of a doctor, especially when your thinking is in disarray. Especially since I questioned whether I could even make it to the doctor or even the emergency room before absolute chaos was set off in my mind as I was driving on I-190 towards Worcester where Island Counseling and UMass Worcester are. But I did settle down as the Risperdal did its job as usual, and I continued on in daily life. But I never told Pat Senior about this incident.

CHAPTER 3

SUMMER 2018
AND BACK
TO WORK

Working as a regional sales manager at ACC in the summer of 2018 was enjoyable but challenging – mostly training on versions of information technology (IT) and customer relationship management (CRM) software that were new to me. Plus, I was learning the technical knowledge of this particular product line, capacitors, and how they were manufactured. Not to mention getting to know the customers and sales reps in my territory. All learning that I had done before when starting new jobs.

But I had other things going on in my life at that time. By this time Dee and I had downsized from our dream house to a

Chapter 3

small ranch on a nearby lake – actually Spec Pond in Lancaster, Massachusetts.

A neighbor owned the lot next door to us, which shared waterfront property with our lot, along with a boat dock where we docked our speedboat "Walking on Water." When the opportunity arose to purchase that lot, Dee and I jumped on it. The lot was buildable at one time, but the permits had lapsed; so, knowing that it would become buildable with a little effort on my part, we set out to purchase it by hiring civil engineers and lawyers to close the deal.

Unfortunately, this was happening at the same time I was starting my new job at ACC and commuting one-and-a-half hours each way to Middletown, Rhode Island, near Newport. On the heels of delivering, cleaning up after, and finding homes for a new litter of Bernese Mountain Retriever pups (in reality they're just glorified mutts), staying up late and waking up early – missing sleep isn't good for a person with bipolar – the stress was building. We were also setting final plans on an addition to our little ranch – more civil engineers and lawyers! The summer months, and especially the summer solstice are prime times for a manic episode, as are the winter months for depression. I can get psychotic in either condition though—twice the fun for Dee and me. Doubling the dose of the miracle anti-psychotic, Risperdal, when the boat started rocking, usually headed off these psychotic states until I could see my doctor for a more rigorous plan.

I was prescribed Risperdal almost since day one after being diagnosed with bipolar disorder with psychotic features in July 1995. It arrested the racing thoughts, ideas of reference (thinking you're responsible for tragic events), ruminations (thinking the same thoughts over and over) and grandiose thinking (ideas of reference on a larger scale) of my particular illness by slowing down my thoughts dramatically. It's a second-generation anti-psychotic that was just released the prior year. Although recommended only for short periods of treatment due to its powerful action, my doctors had surrendered to a daily low dose of the drug – I couldn't live without it! The problem with Risperdal and the mood stabilizers is that they do slow down your thinking, which is good; but it makes it hard to keep up with the fast pace of business because of just that, they slow down your thinking! That said, as I mentioned earlier in the book, I was able to earn a six-figure income from 1995 to 2009 on Risperdal and a mood stabilizer, of which I had tried every one available. Combined with twice-monthly counseling sessions and a monthly meeting with my spiritual director, Father LaPerle, from St. Bernard's Roman Catholic Church in Fitchburg, Massachusetts, I managed to stay out of the hospital from 1999 to 2018. The prayers from the men at my Catholic Men's groups, the Men of Saint Joseph, and later the Knights of the Poor Farm, also helped.

As the summer progressed, so did the expectations at ACC. At some point all the training invested by a company should turn into progress in knowledge and increased sales. By this time, I was still on Risperdal and my mood stabilizer was still lithium. I was prescribed lithium after my close brush with ECT in 2011 because it's very effective at treating both mania and depression. The training at work wasn't sinking in as well as I would like because of the mental fog, cognitive and memory losses, and fatigue that lithium can cause, and the sluggish and sedate thinking caused by the Risperdal. I loved the position because it was everything I enjoyed about sales – designing in the capacitor networks to every kind of electronic and electrical high-tech application, learning a new technology, meeting the customers and sales reps, and helping provide direction to this small, profitable manufacturer. By late August, I wasn't satisfied with how well I was retaining all the information that I needed to know to be effective at the job. I knew from experience that, at some point, this would come to a head, and the management would require me to produce more results independently, without assistance from Dana and the other sales managers. As part of my job description, I worked on the phone and by email with the customers to recommend the right product and answer the technical questions required to design it in. I excel at this. The design-in process could be long – three to six months, but I'm very patient. The job that I was laid off from previously lasted only a year because I didn't ramp up quickly enough and had to rely on others too much for such a high-level position. I was afraid this was happening in this job also – I was in a quandary.

That's when I went off my meds! August 21, 2018. I did it somewhat gradually because I know cold turkey could result in immediate relapse, but two weeks was a lot shorter than the three months I would usually employ to get off a med and change to another. Since we had just dropped our youngest daughter off at college the week before, it was the right time to address some of my dissatisfactions in our marriage. And most likely, mine and Pat Senior's decision to reduce the Lithium (so I could perform better) contributed to my poor judgement in totally going off my meds. Also, I felt that I was going to lose this job anyway, so it was worth a try. It was the only strategy that I hadn't tried in all of my years of working with Bipolar.

Things deteriorated quickly as I became manic, then manic and psychotic. Manic is having high-energy, an exaggeratedly positive view of the future, reduced need for sleep and irritability. Psychotic for me are the intrusive thoughts – thinking I'm responsible for events, big and small (ideas of reference). Reading the newspaper, news reports on radio and TV, and especially sirens were triggers for my psychotic mind. Initially, in the first years of my illness, I thought the Afghanistan War was the result of my not praying enough – grandiose thinking, a form of Ideas of Reference. Dee and I were watching the news in our living room in Lunenburg, Massachusetts, when, seeing the expression on my face, she asked "Dom, what are you thinking right now?" I answered her honestly because she was my first line-of-defense with my psychotic thinking. At the time, that kind of thought was hard for me to shake – very believable to me even though I certainly was "praying enough." To Dee, it meant that we needed to call the doctor right away. That's one of the reasons to this day, Dee is very scared of my religious practices – religiosity and its evil cousin scrupulosity. Conversely, I believe that in the end my relationship with God is what saved me from a lifetime of serious mental illness and allowed me to support my family for so long. Bipolar was my cross.

Since I was concerned about my job performance at ACC but couldn't work any more hours because of the daily three-hour commute to and from Rhode Island, Dana re-evaluated my training process to make it more effective. But it wasn't the process that was the problem, it was my ability to absorb the material. As my ascent into the stratosphere of mania and then psychosis progressed, I got more and more irritable. Since this whole process (of going off my meds until resigning from ACC) only lasted two weeks, there was less damage done than in a long, drawn-out drama.

Usually when someone is manic there's a bad-guy involved. In this case, for me, it was the owner of the company, Jim Haley. I remember my first hospitalization in 1995. When I finally woke up in Waltham Deaconess Hospital, the psychiatrist, a young doctor in her late 30s, asked if I remembered what I said to her on being admitted to the hospital. I responded that I didn't remember. "You said: 'I know that I'm sick and I need help, but please don't medicate me so much that I can't think my way out of this.'" Not understanding the significance of my response, she further explained "I've been treating mentally ill patients in this hospital for a few years now, and no one who's in a manic state says that. They all say "Screw my wife, or my doctor, or the policeman who handcuffed me and brought me here. They never say that they're sick and need help." But somehow, I forgot that lesson this time; that it was me that needed help, not Jim Haley. He was a Catholic Deacon at a church near ACC in Middletown, Rhode Island. Being a strong Catholic myself, I liked Jim. But when things started to heat up, I became more and more annoyed with the way he treated the employees (not that my feelings were based on reality). Dee had started to get concerned, and things were coming to a boil with the land that we finally closed on August 27, 2018, and the house addition. I wasn't totally in favor of building a $300,000 addition at our age, on top of our $220,000 existing mortgage; and of selling the land (after we bought it) to her best friend – a little space goes a long way.

Also in that first hospitalization in 1995, while I was in

a deep sleep due to my exhaustion, I had a vision of myself, young, thin, and with a full head of dark hair, dressed all in white robes laying down on an ancient lounge chair overlooking a crystal-clear blue ocean. White-washed columns surrounded me on this narrow veranda. It was like a still photo in my mind, but was my view of Heaven.

The toughest years of my life were related to being over-leveraged on our dream house in Leominster, Massachusetts, so I didn't want a repeat of that scenario. In 2012 and 2013, we were more than 30 days late on our $460,000 mortgage six times! In 2012, I was on disability and playing the role of Mr. Mom, and in 2013, I was working for Emerson as a service technician, which was not the highest paying job I ever had. Bianca had started college, and Zach was attending a private high school. Dee was working this whole period, but she was also spending too much money on vacations, cars, dining out – living as if we were financially okay. And the mortgage was $3700 a month. The anxiety of this financial nightmare hit me the hardest in the morning. I would awake at 5 a.m. and lie in bed ruminating until 6:30 a.m. when we got up. But these crippling thoughts would remain with me throughout the day, resulting in depression and anxiety that lived as a sub-process in my mind as I attempted to live and work. Depression's fatigue is like having the flu or a hang-over every minute of the day, day after day – crushing.

Since I objected to the impending real estate transactions because of the aforementioned mortgage, and because I didn't think Dee's best friend and drinking buddy would be a suitable next door neighbor, I protested. With her positive attitude, she assured me that everything was fine and insinuated that I was being negative about the whole situation. The third complaint that I had was: this addition would require added nights and weekends maintaining and repairing a large house (if we proceeded with the addition), almost the size of the one we downsized from. When I was younger, and Dee and the family were home with me while I dubiously completed my responsibilities around the house in Leominster, I felt accomplished. But by now, the family was spending more time away at weekend softball tournaments and other sports activities, and Dee was spending more time partying with her friends, including her best friend. I felt isolated! I had let my friendships deteriorate long ago for the family, and because I spent so much time on the house (I'm pretty handy) while Dee was enjoying a week every year in Naples, Florida, and too many nights and weekends away with her friends, I was getting resentful. We rarely could afford to hire outside help for jobs around the house because our budget always exceeded our income; the golden handcuffs were securely fastened.

I requested that since we just completed the purchase of the land, and that I started a new job a few days prior, I would delay further progress on the addition for two weeks until I had the opportunity to catch my breath. She objected and responded that if I wasn't going to contact the required contractors, lawyers and civil engineers, she would! She requested the names and contact information of the people I was dealing with, and I provided them to her. Still objecting to the whole idea of the addition, I had no energy to disagree, plus conflict isn't my forte', so I let her proceed on her way. I was out of gas and the meds don't help you communicate in a misunderstanding, they lock you into your own mind.

Stopping into one of the local churches for one-hour of Eucharistic adoration after this incident, I ran into Father Bob, a family friend. My parents and grandparents are very faithful, as you might have gathered, and we knew many solid, reputable priests. We were fortunate in this age of the priest sexual abuse scandal. Anyway, I unloaded on Father Bob about my predicament with Dee, and he quickly provided some valuable advice: if she's going to handle all the work of the new addition, let her! Don't get involved or expend any energy at all! Brilliant! I strongly suspected that without my help this project wouldn't get off the ground.

Before parting ways, though, Father Bob also had some advice for me. He said "Domenic, remember: resentment is like swallowing poison and expecting your enemy to die!" He advised that a little humility applied to the situation would benefit me, and finally, "Let go and let God." I remembered those words of wisdom through the coming months of challenges, trying to learn about humility to restrain my strong emotions, and how damaging an unforgiving spirit is, while trying to balance justice on one hand and forgiveness/mercy on the other. Some people know this balance naturally. Some of us really have to work at it. I don't have much advice for the reader on this topic except to bring the situation to God.

I would later make another appointment with Father Bob after asking him to be my spiritual director, since my former spiritual director, Father LaPerle, was now 94. Although his years of jogging when he was middle-aged had helped keep him in good shape, that wasn't enough to keep him sharp at 94. Anyway, sitting down with Father Bob in his office, he agreed to be my spiritual director. He asked how Dee was, and I responded that things weren't so great. He didn't say much as I sensed the wheels spinning inside his head. Father Bob is a man of few words.

"Would you take this ring and dispose of it the way you would for an object that's been blessed, which it has?" I asked. He asked questions about the ring, and why I wanted to rid myself of it. I explained that Dee had the ring made special for me back in the late 90s when I was doing well at Hyundai. It was special. But the flipside of the ring was that it included a small diamond that I had found on an engagement ring in a strip mall parking lot a couple years before she gave it to me. I had searched for the owner of the ring to no avail. At the time that I found it, however, I was sky-high manic and in a confrontation with the owners of a small sales rep firm that I was working for over a sales contract gone bad. It had been my first bout with mental illness, so the reminder of the ring had always haunted me, even after over 20 years of wearing it. Father Bob had a different proposal as he placed the ring in a compartment in the organizer of his desk. "Why don't I hold on to this ring for a little while, while you decide whether you really want to dispose of it?"

Another bad memory of that diamond ring was in early 1998, when I was the strategic account manager for Hyundai Electronics. Digital Equipment Corporation (a large computer maker at the time) was my account, one of the seven strategic accounts for Hyundai in the world. We sold them DRAMs (Dynamic Random Access Memories) – the main memory of computers – to the tune of $35 million a year. I was in Seoul,

South Korea, as the leader of the semi-annual meeting between the two companies, and Digital sent three representatives to the meeting. I had a counterpart in Seoul, WKi Park, and he had a few co-workers that helped him prepare for this important day-long meeting. Before the 24-hour door-to-door (my house to my hotel room) flight from Boston to Seoul, I was having a lot of trouble with psychosis, and the Risperdal wasn't controlling the anxiety, so my doctor prescribed valium, which I took a couple days before leaving for Seoul. Upon landing at Seoul International Airport on Sunday night, WKi Park picked me up in his personal car because none of the company limos were available, being Sunday. When doing business in South Korea, large companies don't allow you to drive a rental in the country due to liability because a poor, third-world person might throw themselves in front of your car for the insurance money, knowing that the settlement would keep their whole family alive for the rest of their lives.

Anyway, WKi Park brought me to a small Korean restaurant to meet with the three coworkers for final review of the meeting, which was the next day, Monday, starting at 9 a.m. Koreans love to drink, and tonight was no different. This was before I had given up drinking, and we shared boilermakers with our food – bulgogi (marinated beef barbecue), bibimbap (mixed rice), sun-dubu-jjigae (soft tofu stew), and kimchi (fermented cabbage). Pour whiskey into a shot glass, fill a pint glass halfway with beer, drop the shot glass into the pint glass of beer, then guzzle it. That's a boilermaker. I don't remember how many of these that I did that night, but, in combination with the valium and the long flight, I was pretty wasted by the end of the dinner.

Chapter 3

When it came time for them to go home and for me to go to my hotel, one of the Koreans had the bright idea to put me on a local transit bus since it was getting late, and the Koreans had to get home. I remember WKi Park leaving me at the bus stop and directing me on which bus to take. The next thing I remember was WKi Park rustling through the bushes trying to pull me up. I had passed out and fallen into some local shrubs behind the bus stop. WKi Park had gone home, and, lying in bed, thought: "I'd better go find Domenic." My guardian angel Charlie must have talked to his guardian angel to tell them that I was in trouble. WKi Park got in his car and drove back to that bus stop and pulled me out of the landscaping, drunk off my ass. He put me in his car and drove to a 24-hour convenience store, brought me in, and gave me some hot noodles. Then he drove me to my hotel and filled the bathtub. He told me to get in the tub after he left because it would help hydrate me for the morning meeting, which I did. It's a wonder that I didn't drown, but I made it to the meeting the next morning; and we had a successful day, WKi Park periodically bringing me water throughout the meeting.

But my point – regarding the ring – is that Dee had just given me the diamond ring the Christmas before this happened. The ring went into the bushes shiny and new (like newlyweds' rings on their honeymoon) and came out slightly scratched up, not looking new anymore. Another bad experience with that diamond.

But back to Jim Haley: as a deacon, Jim got involved with the addicted; and therefore, with the mentally ill. We had briefly discussed my particular experiences with bipolar, and one time he suggested that maybe I had PTSD. He even recommended a doctor that specialized in it. I remember thinking: "I'm about as far from the wars in the Gulf as anyone could imagine, never mind that I couldn't fight my way out of a paper bag." I'm not a soldier! I have a lot of respect for the men and woman who serve our country to keep us free. I don't take that for granted. Thinking about it, though, I realized that PTSD results from a face-to-face encounter with evil; something I did have experience with in my first nervous breakdown, but more about that later.

Dee knows that when I begin to get agitated, the illness is kicking in because I'm normally a mellow, easy-going guy – my kids call me Daddy O'Marshmallow! But aside from having bipolar disorder, in reality I'm passive aggressive also. I go along with things I don't agree with until I explode. Not that I don't try to express my dislike for a certain person or situation, but I just don't know how to push hard enough when the resistance against me is too great or someone isn't listening. Something else to work on in therapy!

Speaking of Mental Health and the Military, there were 571 deaths by suicide in all components of the military in 2020 (Losey, Stephen). In 2019, there were 6,261 veteran suicide deaths (Miller, Matthew). This is way too many suicides among our active military and military veterans. I don't think too many people are aware of this.

CHAPTER 4

THE "HIT" ORDER GOES OUT

Jim Haley continues to be a bad guy in this saga, but only a minor villain in the overall story.

Since Middletown, Rhode Island, is 90 miles from our home, I would sometimes commute in a 2007 mint green Mercury Milan that my daughter inherited from my cousin Patty. Her brothers, John and Tony, were kind enough to sign it over to Bianca three years prior when she was in college, when Patty had passed away. The car had over 160,000 miles on it but was very reliable, and better than racking up the miles on my 2013 white Ford Explorer.

As time went on, my dislike for Jim Haley had intensified into all-out hatred. In situations involving my mental illness, my annoyance begins with anxiety over an unresolved issue, proceeds to frustration because I know the solution to my dilemma but can't resolve it, and then moves on to anger when the target person causing my frustration doesn't respond. There are only a few of these frustrating people in my life history. Anger isn't all bad in itself, because anger can be an effective defense against the attacks of the world. But when my anger turns to hatred is when I get into trouble, and people start talking about hospitalization. As a Christian, hatred is also frowned upon – "love your enemy," "turn the other cheek," "forgive," "don't let the sun set on your anger," and so on. But applying those clichés doesn't always work for me, and I become a doormat. I've learned to forgive aggressors as soon as possible (sometimes "soon" takes a long time, though) but not reconcile with them until justice is served and trust is rebuilt. Usually that would require an apology and a resolution not to repeat the offense. If someone commits a serious crime against you, it's not un-Christian to expect incarceration in response. We couldn't just forgive a serious criminal and then let them go home. Similarly, for people who hurt you personally, reconciliation should be delayed until trust is restored. Always remembering that a little mercy goes a long way. We all need a little mercy.

In my mind, someone had to do something about Jim Haley, and that someone was me! Unfortunately for me, though, my aggressiveness toward him had caught the attention of Dana and the rest of the management team. I had given Dana's cellphone number to Dee, and Dee's to Dana, because those questions had arisen. They had become acquaintances in years past because of a situation very similar to this at Hyundai 20 years earlier. When Dana called me on a Thursday morning and said he wanted to meet me at a location between my house and the office, I agreed not knowing his intentions. He pulled up to me and got out of his car, and I let him into the passenger seat of my Milan. "Domenic, please review this letter and sign it, so I can bring it back to personnel at ACC." It was my termination letter, and it was signed by Dana! This infuriated me even more because, in my mind, Jim Haley should have been man enough to sign it himself instead of forcing my friend to do it.

I started writing ramblings on the letter and gave it back to Dana, saying "Tell Jim Haley to either sign this letter himself, or allow me to resign!"

The letter came back as an opportunity to resign, and Jim Haley asked to speak with me in person near the office. Looking back, my guess is that he was concerned about me, and given his training as a deacon, maybe he thought he could help me. My intentions were different: I thought it was an opportunity to "fix" Jim Haley, to give him a piece of my (manic and psychotic) mind. Yes, by this time psychosis had set in and not only was he a menace to corporate society, but also to the Catholic Church – we have enough questionable representatives already!

Dana and Jim Haley set up a rendezvous at a restaurant near the office at 1 p.m. the next day. I was coming from Lancaster, which is a 90-minute drive. In my mind, my little mint green Milan had become a large, shiny black Lincoln Continental; and I was the hitman, hypothetically speaking. I couldn't hurt a flea, and it's only me that gets hurt when I'm angry. Stopping at non-descript 7-Elevens to pick up water, Gator-Aid, and Snickers candy bars, I continued my journey, crunching up the plastic bottles and firing them onto the passenger-side floor of the Milan – I was on-the-run! I hit traffic on Route 24 around Fall

River, and I called Dana to inform him that I'd be late, more like 2:00 p.m. More water and Gator-Aid! It was 90 degrees and humid. I remember looking in the rear-view mirror and watching it vibrate because the music was so loud, another sign of mania. The Milan was in good shape for its age, but one annoying defect was the radio dial. The LEDs showing the radio station dial were burnt out, so you couldn't see what station you were on. I kept hitting the "scan" button in search of Classic Rock stations playing music like AC/DC's "Dirty Deeds Done Dirt Cheap" and "Shoot to Thrill," and U2's "Sunday Bloody Sunday" and "Bullet the Blue Sky." But I don't discriminate, I also like dance music – Mark Morrison's "Return of the Mack," Coolio's "Gangster's Paradise," and Kriss Kross' "Jump." But the radio presets did work. I had set them to local Boston radio stations like 92.5 "The River," 107.3 "WAAF Rocks," 97.7 "The Beat of Boston," 101.7 "WROR," and "Magic" 106.7. There was a can of spray suntan lotion in the cubby of the passenger side door, and it was spinning around inside the cubby due to the vibration of the radio bass.

Two p.m. came and went, and Jim Haley called me on my cell phone. It was actually his cell phone – ACC's – and he wanted it back along with my company credit card. He didn't trust me with either, now! As I thought about it then, I didn't trust HIM with a corporate credit card with my name on it! We agreed to meet at the office, as Jim Haley had given up on the restaurant idea.

Giving Jim Haley the phone was a no-brainer to me, but the credit card with my name on it was a different story. With the crisp thinking of my manic and psychotic mind, I came up with

Chapter 4

a solution. I would find a CVS, buy some scissors, cut up the credit card, then hand the pieces to Jim Haley when I confronted him. But a CVS was hard to find, especially since time was of the essence. By now I was folding the plastic card into segments and ripping the card in half by hand then half again, until there were eight to ten pieces – perfection! No CVS needed! The energy that was pulsing through my veins was supernatural. But I never had the intention of hurting Jim Haley or Dana, only to deliver a strong message. I never was violent while manic, spent outrageous amounts of money, had sexual escapades, or went on drinking or drugging binges, like some manic people do.

When I finally reached the office, of which the location was a last resort because they didn't want a scene for the other employees to witness, Dana encountered me and lead me into Jim Haley's office. He was there with a relaxed demeanor, it wasn't his first rodeo either. I only remember him reminding me that, although I informed him in the interview that I had bipolar disorder, I had assured him that I was stable. At the time, I was. He calmly asked for the cellphone and credit card, and I surrendered them to him without resistance. Of course, the credit card was in pieces, which I thought made a statement to Jim Haley; another one bites the dust! The "hit" was completed, and he never knew what hit him. But in reality, he probably was thinking "this guy's out of his mind." Actually, he wasn't far from the truth. The meeting was very brief, and Dana escorted me to my office where all my belongings were in a box – they were prepared.

I left the office and got in my mint green Milan and headed home. But home didn't end up being my final destination that night.

CHAPTER 5

ON THE RUN

D ana must have called Dee, and in effect they had been talking for a while. I didn't have my cellphone any longer, and the last thing she knew was that I was going to work that morning. But having just completed my "hit," I felt my job was complete. That's when I started driving – all over the place. My first stop was in East Boston at a shrine called "Madonna – Queen of the Universe." I had visited this shrine many times in the 25 years prior, before and after flights out of Logan Airport to every destination – San Jose (Silicon Valley), Raleigh, Chicago, and every other major city in the East, Central, and Northwest, including even Minneapolis/ St. Paul. I had also traveled to Seoul 18 times for sales meetings and training during my time at Hyundai and Samsung. All while having bipolar. Supporting a family and keeping my sales quotas in the semiconductor memory business was at times very challenging, especially when my strategic account was bought out by another company, and I would stop here for solace and encouragement. The Blessed Mother is my guide, and she never disappoints.

It started getting late, so I checked into the East Boston Marriott Courtyard using points and my personal credit card. I also bought new clothes—shorts, sneakers, and a t-shirt at a local Walmart like any experienced hitman would do. I threw away my old clothes just to be sure (of what, I don't know). I spent the early evening at the Courtyard bar drinking Cokes and corresponding with the international businessmen who were stopping over there. I had totally quit drinking for 10 years since the doctor recommended it during my third hospitalization in 1999, not good for depression. But around 2010, Dee had convinced me that I could handle two or three beers on weekends just to be social – we're very social. It turned out that she was right, and since then I never exceeded my self-imposed limit. Regardless, I wasn't drinking on this particular night, knowing that alcohol and mania don't mix.

I somehow got a good night's sleep at that Courtyard in East Boston, and now it's Friday. I thought that maybe I could see Pat Senior if I just walked into Island Counseling in Worcester, so I headed there Friday morning. Little did I know that Dee had the Massachusetts State Police tracking my every move through my EZ-Pass Toll responder; now I was the one hunted. I decided that maybe seeing Pat Senior on such short notice would be pushing my luck, so I checked into a nearby Marriott Courtyard hotel in Worcester Friday afternoon using points and my credit card. Little did I know that Dee was tracking my credit card also! I called a family friend who's a lawyer, Janie Lanza Vowles, and asked her what would ensue if the State Police found me. "Domenic, all they could do is check for anything illegal, and notify Dee that you were found. They can't arrest you or bring you in unless you've done something illegal." I got a good night's sleep again in that Courtyard, but I couldn't see Pat the next day, being Saturday. I also had the idea earlier Friday to call a good family friend, retired Monsignor John Doran, formerly from my parish, St. Leo's in Leominster, Massachusetts. "Domenic, I'm serving Saturday mass tomorrow morning at Notre Dame nearby, why don't you stop in after mass and we could talk?"

I attended that mass, and Monsignor Doran was gracious enough to meet with me after. I repeated the whole story about my conflict with Dee to him, and he was understanding and neutral because he loved and respected both Dee and me. He knew us well because not only had he been our pastor, but our children attended St. Leo's School. He was also the associate pastor at St. Anthony's in Fitchburg, Massachusetts, when I was a boy. That's where my family attended mass, although we grew up in Leominster. My grandfather, John Zarrella, and Grandmother, Angelina, had helped establish that parish. My father's whole family: aunts, uncles, and cousins, attended mass there and gathered at Nonna Z's house after. I also went to grammar school at the parish school, graduating eighth grade in 1975. Anyway, the Monsignor listened to me and guided me that maybe I should go home at this point, because Dee was probably worried about me. He also said something that I now treasure: "Dom, no matter how difficult things have gotten for you, you never gave up hope!" Through the darkest days of my life with bipolar disorder, I always saw a glimmer of light in the distance, like a candle in a dark room. And I always followed it. That light was Jesus.

Chapter 5

Now it was about 11 a.m. on Saturday, September 8, 2018. My daughter, Giavanna (Gigi) had a field hockey game that day at her school, Babson College, at noon; and I set out to meet up with Dee at the game, knowing that she'd be relieved to see me since the Massachusetts State Police never did track me down.

I arrived at the game just as it ended at 2 p.m., and met up with Dee and my older daughters, Bianca and Dominique, in the parking lot near their car. I had in my hands a Patriots dog toy that I planned to give to Tom Brady at a Catholic Men's conference that I attend every spring. My intention was to convince the organizers of the conference to invite him to speak at the next conference, and I would present the dog toy to him there. His Father, Tom Brady, Sr., had given a speech at the conference years earlier – he really did! But talk about grandiose!

Dee was understandably upset with me and insisted that I go to the Newton-Wellesley Hospital Emergency Room nearby for psychiatric evaluation. Initially I resisted, thinking I was fine, but my daughters convinced me that it was a good idea. By this time, the switch had gone off between me realizing that I was sick and thinking that I was fine. I agreed to go in order to re-assure them, but I insisted that my daughters take me, not Dee. When the going gets tough and I'm sick, Dee and I clash.

Bianca and Dominique drove me to the hospital, about 10 minutes away, as they questioned my whereabouts for the last two days. I attempted to explain, but inevitably wasn't very clear. We arrived at the Newton-Wellesley Hospital Emergency Room and discussed my condition with the attendants – my daughters assuring them that I needed to be admitted ASAP. This was their first encounter with me in this condition, since they were very young the last time I was like this. The medicine had done its job for 20 years, but now I wasn't on it.

The doctor asked what meds I was on, and I admitted that I wasn't on any, knowing that they could take a lithium level blood test at any time. We reviewed my medical and psychiatric history and my recent escapades. But the doctor could tell that I was having an episode.

Dominique remembers the admission process, beginning with the psychiatrist recommending that I be admitted "for evaluation." I knew what that meant – I was coukoo for coco puffs! I responded that I didn't think it was necessary for me to be admitted, but I asked Bianca and Dominique: "what do you think?" They reiterated that they thought it would be a good idea, and Dominique was surprised that I quickly agreed to it. More locked doors behind me!

The Newton-Wellesley Hospital (NWH) psychiatric unit is a nice place to visit, but I wouldn't want to live there. The hospital is in a ritzy area, so I chose the right town to melt down in. It turned out to be a 12-day experience where I met many characters, patients, being treated. Young and old, college kids to the elderly, we all had different versions of the same diagnosis, mental illness. Bipolar disorder with psychotic features (thinking disorder) was again my diagnosis. I've been very fortunate that since my first day being sick that has been my consistent diagnosis. Not that I like it, but some sufferers either get the wrong diagnosis, or it changes monthly as doctors attempt to nail it down. The medications that you're prescribed depend on it.

When you're first admitted, you don't know what kind of

patients you'll meet. From totally depressed housewives waiting for ECT (shock therapy) to young men flying from a drugging bender exhibiting signs of psychosis, some can be dangerous. You don't want to make eye contact with them, they might think you're the enemy. It's amazing to see the progress that most totally depressed people who are treated with ECT rebound quickly to become the person they were meant to be. But I'm sure that there was much more work to be done when they were discharged from the hospital. On the other hand, I met a handful of people both at NWH and McLean who you'd never know were depressed but were being treated with ECT. Their suffering was hidden, but having been totally depressed myself prior, I knew that they were genuinely hurting. No one would take ECT unless that was their last resort. It's been greatly improved over the years where it takes much less energy to incite the seizure. Much like a paddle to the heart restarts its rhythms, ECT gets the serotonin flowing again. It usually takes daily treatments for six or seven days where the patient can't eat the night before, and meds aren't required afterward for some patients, but more ECT is. Some of the people I met had tried every type of anti-depressant to no avail before resorting to ECT.

Although, like I said, it's much less destructive than in the past, there still can be side-effects. I believe that short-term memory loss is the most common. I once was being counselled by an employee of Mass Rehab to be retrained for employment; they paid for a Certificate in Project Management for me at UMass Lowell in October, 2011. Yes, that was two months after my own brush with ECT. I was still very depressed back then, but my drive to be re-employed was much greater, so I went for the training. Anyway, I digress. I was sharing with the Mass Rehab counselor that I was afraid that ECT might still be an option for me, but I was scared. She told me a story about a former trainee who she advised, who one day came into her office and by the end of the session had forgotten who brought her to the appointment, who was picking her up, and where she lived! Maybe this was an extreme case, and maybe the ECT treatment had saved her life, but this story wasn't very encouraging. Looking back, although my depression was the worst of my life, it was nothing in comparison to the people I've met who've opted for the treatment. They were major league hurting, with a pain that no normal person could believe or endure. I cry for them even as I write this paragraph.

Being manic, however, is the flip side of this dark abyss. Filled with unmatched energy, highly social, and living in a fantasy world can be enjoyable to some. I'm not one of them. First, mania can destroy your family life, or get you arrested. And second, you know that the end result, after you come down, is that major depression awaits you.

Then there are the manic/psychotic patients who, like I said before, can be scary. One such patient at NWH was Dan, in his early 30s, who was very high on something when he was admitted. I had been there about three or four days at that point, and his room was opposite mine. Somehow, I was lucky to be solo in a two-person room, and the payphone was outside my room – yes, no cellphones allowed. I remember hearing Dan yelling at someone on the phone that if they didn't get him discharged, he would have his lawyer father get involved. I think his father was probably relieved that he was there and wouldn't have lifted a finger to get him out. But regardless, Dan did get discharged a day or two later, into the able hands of two Mass State Police officers – Dan had warrants! He had confided to some of us patients about the gunfight he had in Chelsea that got him admitted. Luckily, the gunshots missed.

Another young man was admitted at about the same time as Dan. Ryan was quite the opposite, very mellow and depressed. Ryan was a former D-1 college football star, a linebacker about as wide as a Volkswagen. We got along great because I had played football in high school, although not as successfully as Ryan – I sat the bench. But we could relate on issues like training, playing in tough games against tough teams, and injuries – I think Ryan was hit in the head too many times. He was from Worcester South High School, an inner-city school that we had played when I was on the Leominster High School team. Reminiscing with him about my recent escapades with Dee trying to track me down with the state police using my EZ-Pass and credit card, Ryan also advised me that your cell phone can also be utilized for similar purposes. His advice when being sought by the law: put your cell phone into the bed of a pick-up truck heading in the opposite direction! Good advice for future adventures – NOT.

Ellie was a 26-year-old young woman who suffered juvenile cancer when she was six, but never really advanced in her maturity because it was brain cancer. She had the mind of a 12-year-old and was therefore very sweet and innocent. She shared with me that Ryan, and especially Dan, scared her. In reality, Ryan was about as calm as could be and almost as innocent as Ellie, but his size was intimidating. Dan, on the other hand, could have been dangerous, although I think we were safe in the hospital.

Ellie's opinion was quite the opposite, and she not only confided in me but tended to stay close to me during meals and counseling sessions. Being a father, it made sense that my level of compassion for other people appealed to her. But why she thought I was a good defense against these guys, I have no idea! After many days of this, one of the counselors pulled me aside and advised that I might want to consider pulling away from Ellie a little because, at some point, she had to leave the hospital and face real life. That was a tough decision for me, but I realized that it had to be done for Ellie's sake. She had wonderful parents who, although they were divorced, came to visit her often. Her mother had recognized the closeness we had achieved in a short period of time and expressed her appreciation to me at Ellie's discharge. Another heart-breaking story in the land of mental illness.

Ivan, Hannah, and Nikki were D-3 college athletes – basketball, soccer, and volleyball – at big-name, well-respected colleges. As freshmen and sophomores, their stays were totally unrelated, but their youth was the common denominator. Under tons of pressure to perform in both academia and athletics, maybe the pressure was too much. Nikki had tried to commit suicide, even though she was a top athlete and was getting good grades. It was equally refreshing and sad to have them there. Refreshing to hear their enthusiastic stories of youthful dreams; sad to know they were here with me just beginning to understand the weight of their illness and how to treat it. Maybe their depression was situational, or they were just burnt-out and would be fortunate enough to walk away from it for life. Sometimes that happens.

About my age was Lisa from Southie in Boston. She grew

up in Irish "Southie" when it was the rough side of town, before it became trendy. She was in the hospital for depression and anxiety. If you knew Lisa's life story, you wouldn't doubt for a minute that she should be depressed. She shared in group counseling that she was gang-raped as a teenager on a picnic table in one of Southie's parks, and her daughter was molested by her live-in boyfriend as a teenager, also. How does she go on? Yet she was very strong. She didn't really have a place to live on discharge but had a nephew nick-named McNealy. He would find a suitable place for her to live upon discharge.

As a middle-aged wife and mother, Linda was divorced from her first husband after he became successful and had an affair with her best friend. She had remarried to a caring man who visited her every day. He had a crush on her in high-school and had asked her to the prom. She declined at the time, but now she couldn't live without him. ECT had brought her back so she could resume her life as a mother of three working two jobs as an RN. Education doesn't matter with who mental illness affects, as evidenced by the young dentist who was also there at the time. Enough pressure could drive anyone with a defect in their brain to cause a breakdown. What those defects are, I don't know.

CHAPTER 6

LET THE HEALING BEGIN

The treatment program at Newton-Wellesley hospital in September was intensive and effective. Your days are spent in group counseling with daily check-ins with your psychiatrist, individual counselors, and the social worker who would help you patch up your life with your loved ones in the outside world. The social worker would also set up partial hospital treatment and outpatient appointments for when you're released, and ensure that you had a place to go. These patient and empathetic people could use some resources to ensure permanent housing for patients who aren't going back home. My feeling is that housing is the missing link in this country for the mentally ill; not an institution, but apartments or rooms. Dee had a lot to say to the social worker and, with her input, my stay at Newton-Wellesley would have been much longer if there weren't more severe patients needing a bed.

Twice a day, any patient that wanted to walk to the outside courtyard for 20 minutes of recreation could do so. We had to walk through the more intensive mental health unit where longer-term patients lived, and some were there permanently. It sometimes frightened me in the beginning of my stay to pass through this unit because I knew that some of these patients would never recover; and I always feared, when being admitted to a psychiatric ward, that I would never return to the real world. The wrong doctor, med reactions, or arguments with other patients could always turn the stay into a nightmare and make your attitude worsen to the point of no return. I had seen this happen to other patients but, luckily, it never happened to me. Regardless, there's always that threat lurking over your shoulder. With the two wards adjourning, patients could move up to the daily care unit that I was in, or from my unit move down to the longer term unit with a locked door separating them. It was a scary reality. But never-the-less, we enjoyed our time outside in that closed-in courtyard where we could play catch and walk around in the fresh air. We joked that the administration should provide a corn-hole game to play, and I advised the other patients that we should all suggest corn-hole in our exit surveys. Patients from both wards were mixed during the recreation time, although not many of the longer-term patients were able to participate because you had to be cleared, even on my unit. Seeing the different ways that people coped with their situation was intriguing. Some had hoodies pulled over their heads. Others walked in circles constantly around the outside perimeter. Others just sat motionless in their own tormented world. I couldn't help but feel fortunate that my illness wasn't that severe, which kept me from thinking about why I myself was here and not with the normal people outside. I guess "to whom much is given, much is expected" (Luke 12:48). I sometimes tried to make contact with the more severely afflicted patients, usually to no avail.

Since I was still hypomanic, a lower state of energy than all-out mania, I had no problem opening up in the group counseling sessions. I shared my recent story and my dissatisfaction with life in general, except for my four kids who made life worth living in a big way. They kept me going through all the days of job frustration, overwork, depression, and anxiety. My number one priority, and Dee's also, was the kids. I always respected her for the love, time, and skill she applied in raising them, and for the wonderful wife she was to me until the start of her mid-life-crisis 10 years earlier.

My plea was consistent: more time for recreation, relaxation, and some time for being with my friends. More margin in our finances to release the golden handcuffs, and less drinking and partying for Dee. I knew that she loved me and would never be unfaithful, but what I didn't know was that her way of coping with the pressures of being married to someone with bipolar and the repeated job losses, was partying, spending money, and an addiction to real estate: the things that drove my anxiety but kept her sane. I wouldn't realize this until my treatment at McLean. I had heard a statistic that I can't footnote that said 80 percent of marriages where one person has bipolar end in divorce – she had held on. On the other hand, Dee's way of feeling loved by me may have been unhealthy in itself – my willingness to spend outrageous amounts of money and spend 24/7/365 of my time on her desires would be proof, in her mind, that I loved her. And her withdrawing from our relationship made me pursue her all the more, another unhealthy way of her feeling loved. Either way, whether her reasons for acting the way she did were because of me or because of her, or some combination, the relationship wasn't working for either one of us, although we loved each other very much.

I remember, just before I went off my meds in August, that Dee and I were alone on our boat on Spec Pond. This was a rare moment because we have four kids. It was common for us to stop the boat in the middle of the lake, and let the boat drift as we jumped on and off the swim platform off the stern. This day was no different. We had just emerged from the water when she posed the question, in true Dee form – fearless and direct: "Dom, are you happy?" I responded that I wasn't. I asked her if she was happy, and she said "No, I'm not." "Then do you want to stay together?" I said "Yes." I then asked her if she wanted to stay together, and she said "yes." With her quick wit she concluded, "Then something has to change!" I agreed, and then she supplied me with further information that surprised me. "I haven't met anyone quite like you in my life." Instead of taking her compliment and praising her for her undying love, I thought to myself, "What kind of guy are you going to meet at a dance club with your friends at midnight in Naples, Florida, to compare me to?" I totally missed the point, because I was so hurt for so long.

There were a couple other problems with Dee's offer to improve our marriage. One, was she willing to forego the house addition? Would she respect my request to sell the land to someone else besides her best friend and drinking partner? Could I really, finally at 57, reduce my responsibilities and projects around the house to enable more free time to just chill? After all, we lived on a lake and had a kick-ass boat.

Her 10-year mid-life crisis had started in 2009 when we had both been laid off, and although she found a job quickly, it was not the time to inform me that we were "just married for the kids," and there would be no more intimacy between us. Now, I could almost understand her wanting to start spending more time with her friends. And I could almost understand that, at 47 (at the time) maybe sex wouldn't be what it was before. But the combination of the two at the same time was, for me, distressful. Plus, she had stopped wearing her wedding ring. I knew Dee well enough to trust her, but these actions left my imagination wondering.

Not to mention that I distrusted the leader of her little posse, her best friend. As with any "good kid" teenager who hangs around with the wrong crowd, Dee's friend wasn't exactly hating the attention of men at the dance clubs and beach parties. Not that she would cheat either, but I felt that she had become a wedge between Dee and I. She would subtly hint to me that she, Dee, and another friend were going to "grow their hair long" to look younger as they started their attempt to live a more exciting life that didn't include me or the other two husbands. She also wasn't afraid to mention the unwelcome advances of the men whose paths they crossed while on their excursions. If she was saying these things to me about Dee, I can only imagine what she was insinuating about me to Dee in their girl-to-girl talks over a glass of wine, or five. Not that I totally disliked her, as I was the one who introduced Dee to her many years before, but I felt deeply hurt by the way she was acting.

Chapter 6

Dee's best friend is a few years older than Dee. But it was when she turned 50 that this whole thing started and would terminate when she turned 60 – that was the plan. Not when Dee turned 60, but when her friend did. Now that she turned 60, it was time to end the escapades and patch up their relationships with their husbands. The plan centered on Dee's best friend, not Dee. Would I want the rest of my life determined by the whims of her best friend, living right next door to us?

Aside from counseling for the issues that I had with Dee, and going on at Newton-Wellesley Hospital at the same time, was the adjustment of my meds. Since I despised lithium and had been on another mood stabilizer called Lamictal before my deep depression in 2011, I wanted to return to it. My thinking was that finally I would take Pat Senior's advice and semi-retire on disability and substitute teaching, which I love. The stress reduction from doing this would allow me to reduce the strength of my medication. Lamictal was thought to be by some as less potent. Dee was included in this group of wise thinkers because Lamictal didn't prevent me from losing my mind in 2009 during the Great Recession, resulting in that deep depression and brush with ECT in 2011. I couldn't blame her, but when I was on Lamictal prior (in the years 2005 to 2009) my head was much clearer and my weight 40 pounds lower than when I was on Depakote, another mood stabilizer that I despised. I was on that mood stabilizer from my hospitalization in 1999 until 2005. I had tried them all.

Regardless, I was prescribed Lamictal, and the doctor started to ramp it up. In addition, tried-and-true Risperdal was its partner as the anti-psychotic in my treatment cocktail– increasing the dose from my usual one mg up to four mg to break the mania. In my past, I had taken up to six mg of this miracle drug because my psychosis was so bad. That's a very high dose.

Since I had gotten the diamond ring back from Father Bob – I knew he held onto it for a reason – I was now wearing it. He had blessed it before giving it back to me in his office. On Sunday, the counselor asked me and all the other Catholic patients if we wanted to attend a Communion service in the cafeteria. I attended that service, and it was beautiful given the backdrop of where it was, the desperate surroundings of a mental ward. Only a few patients attended. One of them was Bob, an older gentleman who expressed his gratitude to that multi-faith minister of the hospital, who was Catholic. I had met with other inter-faith ministers in that hospital stay who were Protestant and Jewish. At the end of the Communion service, I asked the Eucharistic minister to bless my diamond ring, which she did.

Also in the upcoming months, when I was being treated at another hospital, McLean, I would learn another reason for Dee pulling away from me in years past, which was my own doing. The events of my first nervous breakdown were very religious and spiritual. I had the not-uncommon Jesus complex, where I thought I was Jesus, but on that day in July 1995, I also thought the world was coming to an end. Since I was Jesus, and I was having trouble with my boss at the time over a sales contract gone bad, he was Satan. Now, I was new to this whole realm of mental illness, mania, and psychosis, and I had no idea that it ran in my family – remember, this was 24 years ago. So let's follow the thinking process going on as a storm in my mind as Dee watched in horror. Until this time, from when we met in

Chapter 6

1985, I was a normal, fun loving, sincere guy who shared many interests with her. But on this day, something was wrong. She convinced me to take this particular Thursday off from work to regroup and take a break from the conflict at work in the small sales rep company that I joined as my first assignment in sales. As Dee and I clashed that morning, at a time when she was a stay-at-home mom with our two very young daughters, I called my father to go for a ride to calm down; he was always a calming influence.

I explained to him that Dee and I were arguing, and he recommended that my mother, Florence, visit the house to mediate between Dee and me. He felt that she was more suited for the job. Mom came over just as chaos was set off in my mind. When I would be near Dee or my mother in the family room in our house in Lunenburg, I was calmer. But if I went into another room or got away from them, I felt more and more conflicted and wanted to run from the house. Getting in the car and driving close to Boston to confront my boss, the enemy of enemies, wasn't out of the question at this time. After all, it was the end of the world, the final confrontation between Jesus and Satan, me and my boss. I also felt as if this was a judgement-in-miniature, and I was on the wrong side of that equation in the grasp of forces that I didn't want to be associated with. Scary is an understatement, and I couldn't release myself from it on my own power. Paranoid is a better description, but even that word cannot describe the total loss of freedom I felt in this condition. I was being sucked into the vortex of Hell on earth. Yes, at this point I learned that Hell really does exist, and I was headed for it although I'm a "good person." At some point, though, the proverbial lightbulb went off in my head that murder wasn't the solution, and the influence of Dee and my mom was making more and more sense. I had always experienced some level of self-doubt in my life, which made me struggle at sales, but was a great help in this instance – I didn't believe the strong thoughts in my head. Some people in my position wouldn't have reacted in the same way as I had. A straight jacket and strong meds would be the only solution for them, if they hadn't done more serious crimes already.

That's when my mom grabbed both my hands, face-to-face looking directly into my eyes, and said, "Dom, do you remember how to say the Hail Mary?" I responded that I didn't, and she suggested that I say it with her as she led me. "Hail Mary, full of Grace, the Lord is with thee. Blessed art thou amongst woman, and Blessed is fruit of thy womb, Jesus. Holy Mary, Mother of God, pray for us sinners now and at the hour of our death, Amen." She then asked if I wanted her to call an ambulance to help me out of this situation. My fight-or-flight condition ended, and I wanted help, so I agreed to surrender to an ambulance ride, not knowing what laid ahead of me. A police officer arrived at the door followed by two ambulance attendants. They asked me if I wanted help, and without resistance on my part, they led me to the ambulance outside in the driveway. Once in the ambulance, the attendant asked if I wanted to take a shot of medicine in my arm to calm me down, which I accepted. But before the medicine could take effect, my brain was intruded by thoughts that we'd never make it to the hospital because of the chaos in the world due to the end of time – accidents, bombs, gunfire, and all-out rebellion. Armageddon! But that never happened, and we made it to the Leominster Hospital Emergency room shortly after.

Chapter 6

Literally, a padded room awaited me, as Leominster Hospital was simply a transit point between the ambulance and a psychiatric hospital. A counselor from the local LUK Crisis Center interviewed me, but I don't remember the details of the conversation; probably the usual questions about whether I wanted to hurt myself or somebody else. I do remember my father visiting me in that padded cell, giving me a huge, powerful hug. I didn't know he was that strong. But as a father myself, I can only imagine the pain he felt for me as I thrashed with the emotions of a nervous breakdown. I ended up at Waltham Deaconess Hospital because my health insurance covered it, and that's where I had the conversation with the doctor about needing help but not wanting to be medicated too much, and had the vision of Heaven with me in white robes. I had experienced Heaven and Hell in the same day!

But that point of saying the Hail Mary turned my thinking around. The scenario I just described is just another reason for Dee resenting my religious life, even though I don't think, to this day, she knew exactly what was going on inside my head. In the next few years, I leaned more and more on religion, sometimes too much, as it was my coping mechanism. It wasn't just a simple return to normal religious life. But if you had the same experience that I had that day in 1995 in my living room, you might understand. In my religious travels, I also heard the phrase "the only thing stronger than fear is faith," and I was very afraid. The other reason that I turned so strongly toward religion is I was trying to return to the safety I felt in my young years, going to mass on Sundays and visiting my Nonna Z's (Angelina) house after for coffee (for the adults), soda, and Italian anisette cookies with all my aunts, uncles, and 26 cousins.

I'm not so sure it was only psychological and biological, but also spiritual. On the other hand, Dee kept encouraging me to pull back on religion, especially since one of the leaders of my new Catholic Men's Group had suggested that I was "possessed," which I told Dee in my honesty.

So, after more years of trying unsuccessfully to convince me to restrain the rigorous Catholic practices and regain our closeness, she gave up and resorted to her friend's invitation to start the party and not look back. I had resorted to religion as my coping mechanism, her to partying, in response to me pulling away from her and living with bipolar. Looking back, I regret my decisions, but I was scared and trying to get control of a bad situation while being the sole breadwinner in a stressful field.

This is my interpretation of the situation, after the intensive counseling of Doctor Solomon at McLean hospital in February 2019, flashing forward. Doctor Solomon was unusual; in our daily visits he would listen to me for 10 or 20 minutes, then ask one pointed question about what we discussed. In one particular session, I was complaining about Dee's partying and how I begged her for 10 years to stop. He responded, "Domenic, did Dee ever ask you to do something where you didn't listen?" Back at my room that night I realized, finally, that for years before Dee started partying, she had tried to convince me over-and-over to restrict my religious practices because they scared her, and I didn't listen. They got in the way of our once close relationship. She had almost given up.

Now we wonder about those psychotic individuals on the evening news who, in some misunderstood way, think that some unfortunate individual who cut them off in traffic is the enemy and assaults or murders them. Or those that commit these mass killings that plague our nation today. I'm not perplexed that this could happen given my own experiences described above. People are important. Relationships are important. Concern and empathy are important. Love is important. When those things are missing in a person's life, there can be nowhere to turn except disaster. I had Dee and my parents.

There's another explanation that I have for the actions of psychotic individuals, although much more controversial. A couple years before the incident in the living room of my house, around October 1993 (21 months prior to my first nervous breakdown), Dee's best friend and her husband invited us and three or four other couples to all meet with a psychic at their house. We all went in to meet the psychic individually, and this was the first time I had ever done anything like this. It was presented to us as a form of entertainment and seemed innocent enough. Being away from my faith for over a decade, something was bound to fill the void. Wanting to know the future and resorting to occult practices to do so is frowned upon by the Catholic Church, as I would find out later. When I went into the room to see the psychic, she introduced herself as Julia and asked me to sit down at a small table across from her. She asked a lot of personal questions and pulled out her tarot cards, dealing a few of them like we were playing poker. She asked me to pick one up and show her, but it was an insignificant piece of information. The second card that I selected fell out of my hand onto the floor as I flipped it over. It was a black card of some sort, and I gave it to Julia. She looked surprised and said that she wasn't expecting that!! She proceeded to tell me that I would leave my current job as a component engineer and start a new career in sales, but it wouldn't go well. She asked if my current boss was an alcoholic, and I said that he wasn't. Her advice was to beware of my next boss because he would be an alcoholic, and I would have trouble with him. Now, at this time I wasn't even thinking of leaving my current job because Dee was still working. We had one daughter, Bianca, and Dee wouldn't ask to quit working and stay home with the kids until just before our second daughter was born. Julia informed me that she saw a bright light around my aura, and that things would be alright eventually, but I rejected the whole thing. Ironically, Julia presented me with a set of rosary beads and a pamphlet on how to pray it, which I do to this day; a paradox.

Whether you believe me or not, her fortune came true. I left my job the following October when Dee approached me and exclaimed that she wanted to quit her job and stay home with the kids. Our second daughter, Dominique, was on the way. She said she would "clip coupons" to make ends meet when I reminded her that what she was proposing would cut our income almost in half. We had just bought our second home in Lunenburg, and I was remodeling it. So I took a better paying job in sales. Nine months after that I would confront my bosses, including the alcoholic, about a sales deal where my cut would be about $250,000 a year. Since I was on "guaranteed" income for only 12 months until my commissions surpassed my guaranteed salary, I was running out of time. But they didn't want to pay me on this deal, leading up to the conflict and eventual meltdown in my living room in 1995 described previously.

Although my friend at the Catholic Men's group was wrong about me being "possessed," my encounter with that psychic opened a portal to unknown spirits in another dimension who would torment me for years to come. I'm not saying that everyone who sees a psychic will become psychotic; some genetic physical defect in my brain (one of the building blocks of bipolar disorder) would make me more susceptible. The mind is the pathway to the spiritual world, and similar to how a person with Asperger's has amazing genius, individuals with bipolar can have strong mystical spiritual or religious inclinations, good or bad. I would only overcome the bad ones now through confession and receiving the Holy Eucharist; Jesus' Body, Blood, Soul, and Divinity. A simple return to religious practices. There's nothing stronger!!

It's equally important to understand that there isn't always a spiritual dimension to Mental Illness – in most cases there isn't. Medication and counseling are the solution.

Upon discharge from Newton-Wellesley, I returned home. The social worker scheduled a partial program (day counseling) at Marlborough Hospital and marriage counseling at Island Counseling with Doctor Remilard, who worked with Pat Senior. At some point during this time, the brakes locked up in the Milan, literally, and I reluctantly brought it to a Sears Automotive Center to diagnose it. It needed a total brake job, which cost $1200. Knowing that a huge argument would ensue if I asked Dee for the money, I simply took it out of my disability pay that was set aside in the bank to pay the mortgage. During one of our counseling sessions, Dee told Doctor Remilard that I was stealing money and went on a spending spree, like some people with bipolar do. This took the focus off the marriage problems, as Doctor Remilard wanted to investigate this further. I was on the defensive. Showing them the receipt from Sears didn't help convince them either. So, after three or four twice-monthly sessions, the marriage counseling wasn't working for its intended purpose – to bridge the gap in our relationship.

Huck and Moody, my two closest friends, would bear the brunt of my rage against Dee. Moody was a good listener, and a couple beers at a local watering hole would easily equal an hour session with a trained psych counselor. On one occasion when I was dumping on Huck about Dee, he exclaimed "Domenic, I've heard more f-bombs from you in the last two hours than I've heard in 40 years of knowing you" (we met on the football team as sophomores in high school). To this day he calls me "F-Bomb Dom."

I attended the partial program at Marlborough Hospital upon discharge from Newton-Wellesley because it's closer to my home, in what ended up being a six-day course. Patients run in and out of the program as needed, so there are always fresh characters in the mix of eight to ten patients. Two of these were Jason and Brandon. In their late 20s, both unmarried and still under the close guidance of their parents because of their mental illness, they had never "launched." Jason's desire was to be an architect, and he was always drawing buildings and structures in arduous detail. But his parents thought this idea was pie-in-the-sky and were attempting to place him in a more defined career space like accounting. He resented that. He also resented the fact that they had "Section-Twelved" him into the hospital by tricking him to go to the hospital and then getting him committed. Now, I only heard one side of the story, but Jason seemed sincere. I got the strong impression that his parents were controlling him, taking advantage of his mental illness to run his life. This idea of people controlling other people intrigued me. Especially the weaker in our society like some of the mentally ill, the elderly, and teens who are attempting to break into young adulthood. Many times these attempts to control result in rebellion, like drug use for teenagers and violence for adults. I noted this and continued on in what would be a beneficial treatment. Of course, there are people in these situations who do need to be controlled – jail time, being committed, strong consequences for teenage drug use, etc.

Being a people-pleaser who doesn't like to make waves, I was still going along with selling the land to Dee's friend, who called a meeting over dinner at a local restaurant. We had a drink at the bar while we waited for our table and had cordial conversation as we always did. We were seated, had another round of drinks, dinner, and then started discussing the land deal. Since in my social life, I could have only two or three drinks per day on weekends only, I would follow along with the pace for the first couple drinks. Then, when my social acquaintances had a couple drinks in them, they wouldn't notice that I had started to slow down, drinking seltzer water or Coke instead of the usual beer. I'd save one of my precious drinks for later, in case someone called a toast or pressured me to "have one more." This strategy worked like a charm for all these years, and for some people, including my close friends, I would tell them the reason why I had cut back. For other friends, my closest friends, like Mike, Mike, Mike, and Mike... and Mario, they knew the exact reason for my drinking, or non-drinking habits, and understood. No pressure. Bells, Headly, Moody, and Huck are the four Mike's, as we have called them since high school. Mario was the one-and-only Mario.

The discussions about the land deal progressed at that restaurant, and Dee's best friend presented a contract for a purchase and sales agreement on the land. I looked carefully at the document, since it was always me that took the lead on these types of issues when Dee and I were considering them. But before signing the contract, I brought up a couple questions about our tenuous relationship. Feeling that the men in our social group of six (three couples) had become more like back seat occupants in all the girls plans, I raised the issue. Being the positive thinkers that the girls were, they assured me and the other husband (only two couples were at this particular meeting) that this would be the greatest thing since Michael Jackson. I had my doubts about them living next door. Dee's drinking would only accelerate, and our marriage deteriorate under Dee's friend's leadership, and no doubt she was the leader. But what I expressed my concerns about was how I felt that my life had sunk into the low position of being the support and drive behind the girls' dreams and aspirations, not my own. I was assured that this wasn't the case, so I called on the other husband for his input since he had been quiet during the whole meeting. His response shocked me. "I've lost my identity! I can't make a decision, even a minor one, without consulting my wife. And I never see my friends anymore." Talk about being controlled!

I was outraged! I knew that Dee had to take the lead in our relationship and the decisions we made because of my bipolar, but why did this guy have to do the same with his wife? At one point, he was a hard-working, independent thinker who had many things going for him. So much so that Dee had hired him

Chapter 6

in a high-tech company working for her, and Dee always admired the work he did around the house on projects like building decks, remodeling kitchens, woodworking, and yard work. All the things I was trying to cut back on. I exclaimed my feelings that although I hadn't lost my identity because I kept my faith in the face of these pressures, I was losing ground to my wife and her friend. I started dropping f-bombs in the restaurant, not directed at the girls but about the sad situation life had become for us guys. It was getting close to closing time, but the restaurant had cleared out, and I wondered if it was because of my foul language and being so loud.

Leaving the restaurant, Dee excused herself to visit the ladies room, and her friend approached me and offered that if I ever needed a mediator between Dee and myself, she was up for the job. The last thing I wanted or needed! She wasn't listening that she was a big part of the problem—my feelings denied again. Not only was I a codependent of Dee, but I was a codependent of her best friend. Dee had more influence over me, but her best friend had more influence over Dee, indirectly leaving me under her control. I couldn't break through this complex web to deliver the message that I opposed selling the land to her. I define codependency as being controlled by someone so much that you do things for them that you disagree with, all the while smiling and praising how great they are. Like the wife of an alcoholic who buys her husband beer on the way home from work. But somehow, we contribute to our own madness by resenting the person who is controlling us. Like that young doctor pointed out to me in my first hospitalization when she said that most, if not all, patients entering the mental ward are seething mad at someone. I think this resentment and hatred is what allows others to control us; without it there would be no control. So we do have some major responsibility for the situation, but the good news is that it's in our power to release this grip with God's grace – Love your enemy in a radical sense!

Real estate was another codependency for me with Dee – I didn't want the addition or to sell the land to her best friend, but I went along with it. We never did sign their purchase and sales agreement that night.

Discussing the whole situation with my 86-year-old mother and 90-year-old father, my mother offered some pointed advice – tell Dee that you won't sign for the land sale or the addition! Brilliant! Very similar to Father Bob's advice in that parking lot outside St. Cecilia's church. Why don't I think of these things?

CHAPTER 7

MEDS?
WHAT MEDS?

The land, the addition, the marriage – a lot of pressure for someone just leaving treatment. Now you know why the doctors recommend that you don't make major decisions for nine months after leaving the hospital. Plus, it takes about six months to regain your composure and let the meds do their job. New research also suggests that with six to nine months of rest after a nervous breakdown, severed neural networks can develop new connections, increasing your brain function. I would never know, since I always returned to work shortly after an episode.

Marriage counseling simply wasn't working because the discussion always focused on me and my bipolar and not on the marriage issues that were bothering me. The price we pay for getting so upset. And going off my meds didn't help with my credibility. The marriage counseling sessions usually ended in a fight, so at some point we stopped going.

The day before Thanksgiving, my son Zach, who had taken up fishing and being outdoors, shot his first deer in Upstate New York. In his first three days of hunting ever, he got this buck. I was very proud of him for pursuing his dreams of someday becoming an environmentalist, and I still have the selfie he took with the deer in the woods after he shot it. He brought the deer to a butcher nearby, and a week later we both travelled to New York to pick up the meat and the deer head. We took his 2007 GMC Sierra 4x4 pickup truck that he and I had rebuilt. Dee and I had a huge argument about getting the head mounted because of the cost: $600. But I was determined to do it because this was one of the rare forms of masculinity in our house in a long time. I found a taxidermist in our town, and Zach and I brought the deer head to him. I was hypomanic at the time, and my guess is that Dee recognized that mounting this deer head meant more to me than simply celebrating Zach's achievement. I think she was right.

Zach with his first Buck

Chapter 7

Looking for an alternative place to live to allow things with Dee to cool down, my friend Huck, the one who had the by-pass surgery, offered that I could stay with him and his new wife Dawn for a while (they got married at age 56). With no kids, no dogs, and a slower pace, their house was quite relaxing, and I got a lot of rest. But after three nights of dinners together and long talks, I decided not to stay longer with these recent newlyweds.

There's a Benedictine abbey not far from my house in Still River, Massachusetts, and being in a beautiful country setting, I also had stopped by there many times in the past. So one cold, November day I was sitting on the breezeway outside the chapel, and Father Anthony passed by. I had been introduced to him at my aunt Pat's funeral a couple years before. I reintroduced myself to him, not knowing that he lived there because my Aunt lived closer to Boston. He would travel from Still River to Mass General in Boston to be the hospital chaplain years ago when Aunty Pat worked there as an administrator. That's where they became friends. So it was a total coincidence that I saw him there. He didn't remember me but did remember my aunt. I asked him about staying at the abbey because I knew they had retreats there, and he directed me to a priest named Father Augustine and gave me his cell phone number. Although I was a little surprised that the monks had cell phones, I was relieved that Father Augustine was just a phone call away because Father Anthony didn't know his whereabouts. Only about a dozen monks live at this location, but it's a large compound with many visitors and lots of activity. So Father Augustine would have been hard to find.

Father Augustine was open to the idea of me spending some

time there on a self-directed retreat. I was honest with him about my situation at home, that Dee and I were having some troubles, and I informed him that I had bipolar disorder. He could understand as I discussed with him that the pressures on a traditional Catholic family are extreme today. Having four kids and a wife/mother at home for the majority of their childhood is frowned upon by most feminists, her best friend included, who believe that a woman can "have it all," and that any husband whose wife stays at home is an old-fashioned Italian, or a controlling husband who needs to be corrected. I had witnessed this myself, although I married an independent woman who had a bachelor's degree, and it was her wish to stay at home when our second daughter arrived. Regardless, Father Augustine told me to come back in a couple days and he would have a room ready for me.

Staying at the abbey was a gift because of the serene setting and the religious activities of the community. Father Augustine showed me to my room, a simple four walls with a single bed, two bureaus, a desk, closet, and private bathroom. The room was cold initially, but an electric heater helped when someone occupied the room. It looked like the furniture and decorations hadn't changed since the 50s, but I was fine with that. A crucifix on the wall and one window, overlooking a beautiful sprawling field that led down to woodlands of the Nashua Valley. The view of the mountains miles away was breathtaking – after all this was New England in late fall after the leaves had fallen. Father Augustine provided me with fresh linens and a schedule of the daily events – 6 a.m. Matins & Lauds in Latin (morning prayer), 7 a.m. mass in English, which outside patrons attended before work, 8 a.m. community mass (Latin), 12:30 p.m. Sext (Noon Prayer) in Latin, 2 p.m. Rosary, work-related activities around the abbey for the afternoon, 6 p.m. Vespers (evening prayer). 9 p.m. Compline (night prayers) ended the day. I attended daily mass plus some of the Lauds and Vespers. The monks were very helpful about providing the English translations of Latin, so I could follow along. The weekend included Saturday morning confession and a variety of masses, but being in the Tridentine rite there was no Saturday evening mass.

The abbey was established in 1958, but the main house was built in 1683 and is on 25 acres with a separate Catholic religious community adjacent. The quarters I was staying in accompanied about eight other guests, but there were only two other people at this time: a man named George, in his late 60s, and a woman named Carol, in her late 40s. The abbey provided three homecooked meals a day, and since I wasn't working and was paying the mortgage with my social security disability, the budget was an issue. I made arrangements with my brother Fred to contact Father Augustine to pay for the week—$30/day times seven days, or $210. But I didn't need much else except gas money for the Milan to visit my mother and father.

I went to confession on Saturday morning with Father Anthony, the priest who knew Aunty Pat. Confession was held in the original house of the Abbey in what looked like it was the priest's offices. Oriental rugs, again earlier furniture, but clean and well maintained. Father Anthony was warm and welcoming. As I shared with him that I have bipolar disorder, he shared that his father and some of his siblings also had the disease. He was lucky enough to have sound mental health himself but knew the disease well. We had a good talk as I made my confession. I shared with him that I believed that the disorder can have a spiritual component, but I've never found a priest that would confirm this. Only once did Monsignor Doran share that "the mind is the seat of the soul" when I asked him why people with bipolar disorder have such religious experiences. It was early in my disease at that time, and I was hospitalized and desperate for some answers, probably the only reason that he gave me this glimpse into the spiritual world.

I appreciated the quiet of the abbey and got some much-needed sleep while I was there. Since I didn't attend all of the religious activities, I had time to walk the grounds in the crisp November air. Brother Justin told me about a small chapel down in the woods, about a half-mile away, in the back. I put on my hiking boots and wool socks, long coat and jeans, and a stocking hat with warm gloves, and hiked to the chapel. It was a wide dirt road that led me there, and some of the wildlife was still active in these woods. Squirrels with large furry tails and a few various birds. The trees were bare, and I could see my breath as I made my way to the chapel, called the Knoll because it's on a small hill. It's dedicated to Our Lady of Guadalupe, and I was told that it was built by Brother Joseph in the 1960s. It had a large wooden front door with an iron door handle and a large keyhole. When I tried to open the door, it wouldn't budge. Upon returning to the abbey, I spoke to Brother Justin, and he confirmed that there's a key to the chapel that I could take on my next voyage.

Around this time, before Christmas, my 90-year-old father's health started to deteriorate. He had stopped the Lupron treatments for prostate cancer for a better quality of life since the cancer had metastasized and was now in his bones. Lupron reduces a man's testosterone, so my father had been very fatigued for the last eight years during his treatment. It was hard to watch this gentle man suffer. Anyway, this gave me a good excuse to stay with my parents for a little while and help my sister Angela, who was also living there for a brief time to help with my father. In addition, dementia was setting in for him, and he started to wander. Having been healthy all his life, this was an adjustment for him. My mom and dad, my sister and myself were living in the house I grew up in, nearby in Leominster. Now two of our kids were out of college, and the other two were away at college, so I wasn't missed much at home.

On one particular night Angela and I were talking as our parents slept. She had been divorced many years earlier after having three boys, then she worked for the Veteran's Administration as an LPN for 20 years before retiring just before reaching 62. She had recently sold her house in New Hampshire, so my parent's house was a stop-over before deciding her next move. Also, my parents could use some help with their health, especially from a nurse. We discussed my parent's health and where this was all heading for them, knowing that Papa wouldn't have long to live given his cancer diagnosis. As we talked about life in general and my situation in particular, I was still boiling mad at Dee and somewhat hypomanic still. That's when Angela gave me some good advice – We really can't judge people or their motivations, so resentment is wasted and only hurts ourselves. There's that word again, resentment. It sounded like her and Father Bob were talking to each other, but in effect, they weren't. She was just going off my cues.

Of course, sometimes we have to judge. Like whether to go down a dark alley, or whether we should be associated with certain people because their actions are dangerous. But we don't know the whole picture behind someone's life; and, therefore, need to take a step back before judging them as good or bad people. We can choose not to associate with them and leave the rest to God. Hate the sin, not the sinner.

I continued individual treatment with Pat Senior, and somehow, I was holding it all together, barely. Dee and I continued to see each other regularly since the holiday season is a treasured time in our family.

As Papa grew worse, including falling on the cement front steps of his house and busting up his head pretty bad, someone now had to stay with him at all times. I joked with Angela later on that 70 years of smoking didn't kill my father but sneaking outside for a smoke while no one was looking, then falling on the steps, almost did. After another fall and a bout with the flu that was going around, he ended up at St. Elizabeth's Hospital in Brighton. They were treating him for a bad cough and pneumonia, and he entered rehab after leaving there. My brother Joe, in town from Florida with his wife Sandy, Angela, and I interviewed rehab facilities for Papa to be treated at. We picked a reputable rehab and nursing home in Leominster, and Papa was transferred there from St Elizabeth's – he was not happy! Although not pleased with our decision to put him in rehab, when we explained that no one could keep him safe at home even with all the rudimentary alarms and door-locks in place, he understood. Upon admission, he would approach us each individually asking how we could get him out of there. Papa was a silent sufferer though, so he just kept a low profile and did what the doctors and nurses advised. I remember once getting a call from him on my cell phone while he was at rehab. He pleaded with me to come pick him up and take him back home. I advised him that I was out of town, so to call my brother Fred, who managed Papa's care. I later learned that Papa had first asked Fred to get him released, and when Fred declined, Papa replied "then I'll call Dom," which he did.

Meanwhile, I was still hypomanic even on the increased Risperdal. I started seeing Dr. Remilard for individual counseling – more complaining about Dee. His advice was that, although we can love someone very much, the one thing they do may never change, and we have to make some tough decisions. His examples were: "If only my husband didn't cheat," "Or if my wife didn't drink so much." Pat Senior, on the other hand, had the opposite advice. On one particular appointment for evaluating my meds (400mg Lamictal and 3mg Risperdal), Dee came along with me. While discussing my prognosis, Dee and I broke out in a heated argument. Dee is part Irish and very fiery. I'm 100 percent Italian and very passionate. We sometimes clash. After witnessing this Worldwide Wrestling Federation match right in her office and trying to recap our visit, Pat said "I see a lot of frustration and anger on both of your parts, but I don't see 'I hate this person, and I don't want to be married to them for another second.'" She was trying to say that we still loved each other – another theme that I would hear repeated a little further on in this whole story.

Christmas was merry, even though I wasn't living at home. I was living with my parents. The four kids were staying at the house; Bianca and Dominique from their apartments in Boston, Zach was on semester break from Purchase College, a State University of New York, where he played lacrosse, and Gigi from Babson College, where she played field hockey, like her sisters had at Vassar and Tufts. Dee and I agreed that I would stay at the house for Christmas Eve and Christmas night. We hosted Christmas Eve as usual with my parents, my sister, her son Matthew and his fiancé Savannah, and my brother Fred and his girlfriend Barbara. Rob, my youngest brother and his wife Linda from San Jose, also joined us for the traditional Italian seven-fish dinner, although we usually had about four or five different fishes that Dee and the girls cooked. My job was the dishes afterward.

Having had a late night on Christmas Eve, it was a while before the family was ready for mass in the morning. The abbey has a noon mass in Latin, so we set out for Still River. Additionally, the abbey was 10 minutes from Dee's sister's house where we would spend Christmas Day. It had long been a tradition to spend Christmas Eve with my family and Christmas Day with Dee's family. Dee's younger sister, Kelly, and her husband Todd, are about five years younger than Dee and me. Their children, Maddy, mid 20s, Zoey, early 20s, and Tatum, early teens, were there for the dinner. Dee's younger brother, Greg, was there with his girlfriend and his son, Casey, in his early 20s. Grammy and Papa, Dee's mom and dad, rounded out the guest list. We had a roast with all the vegetables and salads you could eat, then dessert. As is custom, after everyone else left, Dee and I would stay back with Kelly and Todd for "a glass of wine." I looked forward to these sessions, as they were always open discussions about life in general, and sometimes the more pressing issues. We talked about the separation but only in general terms, not trying to solve the whole dilemma. A lot of laughs usually accompany the serious talk, and a few sentimental tears are always in order on the part of Kelly. Leaving Kelly and Todd's house was always interesting, wondering if the car that I "warmed up" would run out of gas in the driveway waiting for us to finally say good-bye.

For New Year's Eve, Dee and I partied at her best friend's house, as I held my relationship with her, her husband, and Dee in good standing. Lots of other guests were there. For some strange reason that I still don't understand, Dee and I can be ripping each other's heads off during the day, but at social events we always have a good time together. New Year's Eve was no different.

Saturday, January 5, 2019, was a big event for the extended Zarrella family. My Uncle Larry, Papa's youngest brother, turned 80, and there was a huge celebration at the Rye n' Thyme restaurant in downtown Leominster. My first cousins, Laura, Paula, and Peter threw the party for their father, and all 26 of my Zarrella cousins were invited. I saw cousins from every part of the country – Florida, California, Maryland, Washington, D.C., Texas, etc. Papa looked dapper in a suit that Nonna and I had bought him a year or so earlier. He also wore a Baker Boy hat that was classic Papa. I was the only one from my family who attended.

In mid-January, I made another brilliant decision. In my head, nothing was being resolved, and I still had a full tank of resentment. Resentment is the slow-release version of hatred, and I had confessed it to a priest many times in the last 10 years. "Father forgive me. It's been a month since my last confession, and these are the sins I'd like to confess." But nothing had alleviated my pain, and I felt the medicine "locked me in" in my own mind where I couldn't really express myself since a mood stabilizer does exactly that – prevents the highs and lows in your emotions. I was stuck again, stuffing my anger. Not appreciating the fact that my last visit to the cuckoo bin, Newton-Wellesley, had altered my meds from Lithium to my much-loved Lamictal, I went off my meds again!!!

Once again, I went fully manic within two weeks, and on one particular night I visited the house to pick up some things. Dee was there. Going to the waste basket in the kitchen to throw away some old clothes, I noticed that Dee had thrown away a large grocery bag that I kept my religious paperwork in. Articles from the Pope and other leaders in the Catholic Church, and some from Protestant writers. Books, small inspirational plaques, and a Bible. Anyway, I was outraged. She had a glass of wine on the coffee table, so it was just another reason for me to be upset. I approached her angrily about the religious items and her drinking, not in a nice way. I looked her directly in the eyes and said, "You can't throw away my religious things, and you need to stop drinking and get some help right away!!!" The look in my manic eyes is something I later described to Dr. Solomon at McLean as worse than Dee having a gun pointed at her head. I had done this before with a coworker when I was first sick. This scared Dee, and she doesn't scare easily. She had never seen me this way, and my rage was never pointed at her directly. The argument continued until Dee called the Lancaster Police saying that she was frightened by my actions and wanted me to leave. Two Policemen arrived at the door a short time later. Dee was at the door to receive them, and they asked if I had assaulted her. She answered "no," but said she was afraid of me because I never acted like this.

Chapter 7

One of the policemen approached me in the living room and asked my version of the story. I described the incident, that Dee was drinking and had thrown away some important paperwork of mine, and an argument had ensued. Before the police arrived, I was able to take one mg of Risperdal that calmed me down, so as to appear sane. "Did you assault your wife?" "No, I didn't touch her!" "Do you know why she called us?" "Yes, she's scared." The policeman asked me to collect some things and step out of the house. I gathered a few things and walked to the driveway, escorted the whole time by the officer. In the driveway, near my car, he handed me a restraining order and warned that it was valid for three days. She also had told the police that I had recently obtained a license to carry a firearm in the state of Massachusetts, and she feared that I might use a gun in my anger. I had taken the LTC course with Zach months earlier to help him strengthen his resume to one day become an environmental policeman, which he was considering at the time. "You can't be within 100 feet of her." The judge that they called for the restraining order had set up a court date for Dee and me on Monday morning at 9 a.m., Clinton District Court, about 20 minutes away. I arrived at the courthouse afraid of her testimony, and what would happen next. "Zarrella vs. Zarrella" said the attendant. Dee didn't show up for the hearing so as not to get me in further trouble, and the restraining order lapsed. To this day, that's the incident that I regret most, frightening her like that. I think I'll regret it for the rest of my life. I'm so sorry!

Although Dee likes to party, she's not an alcoholic. I was subconsciously accusing her as such to take the focus off me and the state of mind I was in. But this theme would continue throughout this whole saga.

Papa's health had markedly worsened, and my mother had also spent some time in rehab with him. A further decline in Papa's health had required that he be re-admitted to the rehab, with hospice care also. His persistent cough and a tough case of pneumonia were now working against him. I visited him every day, but again, he wasn't happy to be there and expressed that to me constantly. Luckily, by some small miracle, my brother Fred was able to convince the doctors to allow Papa to return home under hospice. A sure sign that he was close to death was that he allowed hospice to set up a hospital bed in his room. He and my mother were accustomed to sleeping in recliners in their later years because it was much more comfortable for them. He didn't like hospital beds but rested comfortably this time as we alerted family to his condition. My brothers Joe and Rob came from Tampa and San Jose with their wives. Angela, Fred, and I are close by. His brothers from nearby Fitchburg, Massachusetts, came to visit him one last time, as did his sister Gloria; Mario is 94 and Larry had just had his 80th birthday party that I attended. Gloria is Papa's youngest sister.

I spent a lot of time with my father in his last days, so no regrets there. I was on Social Security Disability, so I had the time. A few days before his death, Dee visited Papa to say goodbye and to assure him that she and I would care for Nonna after he passed. He could rest assured. Part of our proposed addition would have been a small apartment for him and Nonna, and we promised that now Nonna could live there and move out of their house. The addition was still being discussed at the time, though, and Dee and I ended up in a huge argument. Father Bill from our parish gave him last rites a few days later, and I had placed a Carmelite Brown scapular around his neck, where the Blessed

Chapter 7

Mother promises to take the soul from purgatory to heaven on the Saturday following their death for those wearing it. Papa had been enrolled in the scapular in childhood, not uncommon in those days.

Papa passed away the morning of Thursday, January 17, 2019. Angela called me to let me know. I went to the house and had a moment alone with him. I would miss him, but was relieved that he died peacefully at home, as he had wished. I didn't want him to linger for many more years in a state of dementia living in a nursing home, like his mother, Angelina, did. We notified family and friends and started making arrangements for the funeral with Father Juan from St. Anthony's. As Angela, Joe, and I met with the priest, Fred and Rob met with the funeral director. We all gathered pictures and selected people for the eulogy, readings, hymns, and poll bearers. Papa would have been proud.

Meanwhile, my anger at Dee's best friend was building. Since I had been trying unsuccessfully to convince her to back out of the land deal, I drafted an email to her. Actually, it was very kind. I calmly explained that having her live next door wouldn't help Dee's drinking or our marriage (partying with the girls). She responded something to the effect of: "Domenic, you're family and always will be family. I love you guys and will always have your best interest at heart, living next door or a million miles away!" She then made some demands to the effect that they would buy the land but only go through with building the house if we went forward with our addition. Does she "get it?" Has she been listening to me? Or does she just think I'll go along with this plan to avoid a confrontation? Maybe she was counting on continuing our codependent relationship, but I wasn't. I responded to her by email saying that she would only purchase that land "over my dead body," and that all the positive thinking in the world wouldn't get her the land (she considers herself a positive thinker). Case closed. She conceded that they would pull out of the deal, but in actuality she wasn't done.

Since my pencil was sharp and my keyboard warmed up, I thought that now would be a good time to clear the air with Dee, too. In an email, I reminded her of what she told me 10 years ago about being married "only for the kids," and I also reminded her that our youngest daughter, Gigi, had left for college six months earlier. The kids weren't kids anymore. "Tic-Tok" were the exact words I used to express that our relationship was over, time had run out!

Papa's funeral was coming up in a few days, Saturday, January 26, 2019, and since my emails hadn't gone over too well, I reserved a room at a local hotel for Thursday and Friday nights. The morning of the funeral, Saturday, I sent Dee a text, copying my brother Joe and my daughter Bianca, saying that Dee should tell her friend not to attend Papa's funeral because "Papa wouldn't want her there." I was all-out manic again. My feelings were true, but my delivery left something to be desired. I was anxious about the land deal, frustrated that I knew the resolution, and angry that no one was listening to me. Dee objected to telling her friend not to attend the funeral, and I informed Dee that if she wouldn't tell her friend not to attend, or if Dee told her but her friend attended anyway, that I would walk out of the funeral. She never attended that funeral.

We met at the funeral home that morning, and Dee and I

were at odds, of course. Our family friend, Monsignor John Doran, had attended the wake the night before, Friday night, when Dee approached him to inform him about my behavior. And I'm assuming that she described the emails I had written to her and her best friend, but he never confronted me that night.

The funeral was beautiful in that small church, St. Anthony's, where Nonna and Papa were still parishioners. The church was packed, and I sat next to Dee with the rest of our family. My nephew Matt, Angela's son, gave a great eulogy, and Father Juan did a wonderful job on the homily. Bianca and Tiffany, my brother Rob's daughter, did the readings. Bianca would soon become a medical student, and Tiffany has a doctorate in infectious disease, working for the National Institute of Health. Papa had done a marvelous job as a grandfather also, and his grandchildren's achievement are a testament to that. My father was much loved in the community, so it wasn't hard for people to say nice things about him. I gave a speech at the grave site pointing out how I had keyed off his fathering skills, and that was the one thing I most wanted to be because of his influence. A luncheon at the Four Points Hotel in Leominster followed, and we had a huge gathering of friends and family. My aunts and uncles, Mario and Grace, Larry and Bruna, and Gloria were there, as well as most of my cousins from both sides of the family. The cousins that had flown in for Uncle Larry's 80th birthday party must have been going broke on airline tickets because most of them came back for the funeral, which was only three weeks after the party.

I couldn't stay at my parents' house forever because home health care was coming for my mother and the bed I was sleeping in was needed for the overnight nurse, so an alternative was needed. Back to the abbey. Father Augustine welcomed me back and showed me to the same room that I had stayed at before. "Another week, Domenic?" "Yes, Father, thank you!" Once again, I didn't tell him that I was off my meds.

The week at the abbey was similar to the other week that I had come. Quiet, with more much needed sleep. Although I attended daily mass and some of the other activities, I also spent a lot of time visiting my mother at her home. Unlike the last time I was at the abbey, though, there was a foot of snow on the ground, and it was bitterly cold on the top of that hill, around 15 degrees and windy. I had all the necessary clothes and made another hike to the Knoll. Hiking boots, wool socks, large jacket, stocking cap and gloves, and two or three layers of clothes. Something about that little chapel seemed mystical to me, but I forgot to grab the key before heading out on the 20-minute walk to it. I would never make it back to the Knoll on this visit.

There's a community dining room at the abbey where visitors can go to meet with the monks, have breakfast, lunch, or dinner; and discuss events, religious or otherwise. This kept the abbey fresh, but you sensed there was still a veil between the main abbey and the monks' quarters, especially where the abbot lived and prayed. I never entered that area.

One day I was having lunch and a couple monks entered with one of the regular visitors, all in work clothes. Brother Joseph struck up a conversation with me, and I joked that I would gladly help them with their work, digging a trench between the former foundation of a building that had recently been torn down and the drainage system 50-feet away. They were using a power washer to blast through the frozen ground. This was necessary because water had started to build up in the empty foundation. I said I'd suit up after saying my rosary, and he responded that "work is prayer," so I decided to say my rosary later and join the workers. I remember thinking that Dee would like this monk!

Thursday night was bitterly cold, and I decided to take a walk outside to collect my thoughts in the fresh air. The grounds were dimly lit, and I walked through the neighboring religious community. Sitting down at a bench outside the high school to finish my rosary for the day, a man dressed in brown pants and a large winter coat approached me. "Can I help you?" "Oh, I'm just a guest of the abbey, and I'm taking a walk to get some fresh air, stopping here briefly." "Would you mind sitting somewhere else? There's a convent of cloistered nuns close by, and we prefer that people don't bother them." "No problem," I responded. He directed me to a small chapel across the road where I could get some peace. "It's very quiet, and much warmer." I wandered to the chapel and walked in. The entrance was full of statues and religious pamphlets, the kind Dee would despise because of my religiosity, and I leafed through them. The Housetops magazine, various prayers to saints, and posters for upcoming events. But I didn't collect any. One of the brothers walked in as I was reading The House Tops and asked if I liked the magazine. I responded that the articles were of much interest to me, especially the one about Saint Anthony, my favorite saint. "We write that magazine right here in this monastery." I was impressed that such a small monastery wrote such impressive material.

I walked slowly into the chapel, blessing myself with Holy Water, and knelt down in a pew. "Lord, please bless my family and bring us through these misunderstandings so Dee and I can live in peace. Can't you see that I'm crying???" I sat for a little while, enjoying the calm of the chapel and the low lights, glimmering votive candles, and the crucifix hanging over the altar. A traditional communion rail graced the front of the church. The statue of the Blessed Mother, who I adore, was off to the right. I asked her to intercede for my family and to ask her son Jesus to bless the kids. Feeling a little depressed, with tears in my eyes, I departed the chapel expecting to head right to my room. Back in the entrance was a group of about 12 monks and religious sisters to greet me, and I reiterated that I was a guest at the abbey. The monk that had recommended this chapel recognized me and asked if it was as peaceful as he said it was. I responded that it was, and that I had come to pray for my family because Dee and I were going through tough times. "It's hard to hold a traditional Catholic family together in these secular days, and my wife and I are struggling." One of the monks acknowledged my predicament, and the whole group of them committed their prayers for my family. Their small parochial school was filled with children from traditional Catholic families, some of them with six or eight kids. I felt relieved walking back to my room and got another good night's sleep, remembering how consoled I was to have a whole monastery of monks and sisters praying for my family.

On Friday, I attended morning mass as usual. I ate breakfast, lunch, and dinner at the abbey with the guests. One of the monks always joined us for dinner, and this time it was Father Peter. Father Peter is a little older than me, maybe in his early 60s, a robust man with a wonderful sense of humor. At dinner he talked about why he became a priest after many years as a brother – because he wanted to be able to give people the sacrament of confession, as many people asked him to. Being a monk he couldn't, hence the desire to be a priest later in life. He explained the story that one of the guests at the abbey asked him to hear his confession, mistaking him for a priest. That one single experience encouraged him to go to seminary. After dinner, Father Peter invited me to join him in the living room; he wanted to introduce me to someone. The living room is open to the dining room, making a large area about the size of a small house. Decorated with older, re-upholstered couches and chairs, an oriental rug, and lit by dim lamps, it was warm and very comfortable. I sat at the end of one of the couches, and there were three of four other people in the room, aside from me and Father Peter. "Domenic, I'd like to introduce you to Mike Cutone, he's a Massachusetts state trooper based in the Western Massachusetts barracks. About six-feet tall, very broad shoulders, you could tell he worked out and could probably bench press about double my weight of 210 pounds. Dressed in civilian clothes, the only unordinary feature aside from his size was his totally bald head (hair is optional in the third millennium). He shook my hand firmly, looked me in the eyes, and said he was glad to meet me. "Domenic, Mike has served in the U.S. Army, Special Forces, with four tours in Iraq," said Father Peter. I was immediately impressed!

I was introduced as a father of four, a double E, having had a successful career in high-tech sales developing all kinds of electronic devices, including some of the weapons and communications gear that Mike had used in warfare. Not very impressive to me as I sat in the same room as such a hero. But, for some reason I got the impression that Mike had equal respect for me as I had for him. We were both fathers and husbands supporting our families the best way we could. At this point I wasn't sure why Father Peter wanted me to meet Mike, but as the conversation proceeded, I was clueing in more and more. Mike told his stories about being a trooper, but not much information about his Army experiences. His only comment to the group was that being in combat, the most dominatable enemy is fear. He said that fearlessness is the main characteristic that allowed him to complete many missions unscathed, without even a mosquito bite. Jumping out of planes behind enemy lines, gunfights, and giving aid to wounded comrades, attempting to get them safely to medics, and being in helicopters under fire was about as detailed he got in his stories. Not much more information.

Mike also told state trooper stories: speeding 100 mph after drug dealers and other criminals, pulling over speeders only to find out that they had a handgun, and coming to the aid of officers down. His advice when being pulled over by a state trooper was not to argue with the policeman but to accept the punishment willingly if you had broken the law—maybe he would let you off. I would later use this strategy in the hospital by not arguing with the doctors and counselors when they were calling me out on my actions or attitudes. Father Peter also had some stories about being escorted in a police car at high speeds to give last rights to a dying person and stopping at the scene of an accident to give last rights to a dying passenger. He was a wild man himself.

One of the other people in the room was a young guest at the abbey who was discerning a calling to the priesthood or being a brother in the Benedictine tradition, as were all the other monks here. But why was I in this group of impressive people? Knowing Father Peter for only a short time, what did he see in me that prompted this meeting? The only hint that I was given was a prayer card that Mike Cutone gave me that he had written and printed, about Spiritual Battle:

SIC DEVS DILEIT MVNDVM
Soldiers Prayer

Lord Jesus, I choose to serve You. To fight the good fight, to shoulder my share; to refuse the easy way out. Dear Lord, teach me to accept and carry my cross to the bitter end. During the hardships and ridicule of this life grant me the grace to persevere; the grace to march towards You with every step, every thought, every breath. Even though I stumble or fail... hope remains. Hope in You my Lord will always remain. Victory in Christ. Amen."

MSG. Cutone, Michael

US Army Special Forces

C/1/5th SFG(A) Iraq 2005 - 2006

Mike had one other tip for me before we departed. "The greatest spiritual weapon is the rosary of the Blessed Mother. But in battle you don't always have the time or the peace of mind to say a rosary (a rosary takes about 30 minutes and is meditative), so I say the Memorare."

Memorare

Remember, O most gracious Virgin Mary, that never was it known that anyone who fled to your protection, implored your help, or sought your intercession, was left unaided. Inspired with this confidence, I fly to you, O Virgin of Virgins, my Mother; so to you do I come, before you I stand, sinful and sorrowful. O Mother of the Word Incarnate, despise not my petitions, but in your mercy hear and answer me. Amen.

I put the Soldier's Prayer card in my wallet, thanked Mike for it, and headed to my room praying to God asking for guidance as to where this was all going. Was I heading into a Spiritual Battle?

Before my week was up, the Sunday of my visit – Super Bowl Sunday – where I began this whole book, I had lunch, grabbed a banana, and headed out to my car. It was a cold, dark day, and the Abbot was also going to his car from a different exit from the abbey. Snow had accumulated on the perimeter of the parking lot. We crossed paths, and since I was still holding the banana peel, the Abbot said "don't slip on that banana peel," which I thought was odd. Soon after that is when Dominique called me to meet her and Bianca at Mass General to check on my mental health, and I was admitted before being taken to Mc-Lean. I certainly did slip on that banana peel, right into the mental hospital!

CHAPTER 8

HOSPITALIZED AGAIN

I left the abbey on that cold February day, hoping to get the psychological evaluation behind me in time to watch the Super Bowl at 6 p.m. It was about 25 degrees in Boston that day. Bianca and Dominique were meeting me at Mass General at 3 p.m.. As cold as it was, they would ride their bikes from their apartments. Bianca shared a small apartment with two roommates in the Fenway area of Boston, and Dominique had four roommates in Southie. These two girls rode their bikes year-round from their apartments to Mass General for work and to other locations for social events. In the summer, it wouldn't be unusual for them to ride 20 or 30 miles to the North Shore or South Shore beaches on their bikes; after all, these girls were D-3 field hockey players in college and were trying to stay in shape while working in office jobs. They both worked in the

Gynecological Oncology Department doing cancer lab research and clinical work with cancer patients having surgery – great work for gap years before medical school. Dominique was in training to replace Bianca since she would be off to medical school at the University of New England soon.

The roads were snowy, but I made it to Boston in about an hour and met the girls at the parking lot where I parked the Milan. We headed to the emergency room. The attendant asked my name and why I was there, and I declared that I was there for a psychological evaluation. After about 30 minutes of waiting, the nurse asked me to step into room two; there were three rooms. She took my height and weight and measured my blood pressure and temperature. She asked how I was feeling, and I explained that I was fine, but my wife and daughters suspected that I wasn't. "Do you have thoughts of suicide?" "No." "Thoughts of hurting anyone else?" "No." I really didn't. So, it was on to the next level of the evaluation with a psychiatric nurse.

She asked what was going on in my life, and I explained that Dee and I weren't getting along, and I wasn't living at home. Coming from the abbey might have made her suspect. She assured me that I sounded fine but would recommend that I proceed to the next step, evaluation from a psychiatrist. This took a little more time, so I waited with the girls in the emergency room. We talked about general topics and made conversation about the upcoming Super Bowl, and how we wished this visit wouldn't take too long so we could watch it on TV. We waited about an hour for the psychiatrist to interview me. Not a bad wait for an evaluation – most nut-jobs were probably smart enough to hold off their nervous breakdowns until after the Super Bowl.

Chapter 8

Bianca and Dominique were in the hospital room with me and the doctor when he interviewed me. I complained about Dee, and the pressures that she was putting on me, but I didn't sound homicidal by my own standards. The young doctor asked if I wanted to be admitted, and I assured him that I was fine, perfectly sane! He had a different opinion. "My recommendation is that you be admitted so we can get a better look at you and decide where you'll go from here." I was upset. "I don't need to be here, so I'll go home now, thank you!" He had other plans for me. "If you won't stay on your own volition, I'll force you to stay against your will." I asked if I was being Section-Twelved, and he confirmed that he had seen the emails that I wrote to Dee and her best friend. I was nabbed! I was sure that Dee had set this trap, and it made me angrier and angrier. I would only discover later that it was my two daughters that had asked that I stay. I was stuck. Not wanting to be held against my will, I accepted the doctor's invitation for an uncomfortable bed for the night. But not until after watching the Super Bowl in that emergency room with my innocent daughters. They were getting invaluable training on psychology even though their desires were to be a cardiologist and an orthopedic surgeon. It wasn't quite 6 now, so the Super Bowl hadn't started yet, but the commercials had. At this point we were in the psych ward emergency room with about five or six other patients.

Of course, before entering the psych ward, they had to take any objects that I could harm myself with. "Please give me your belt and shoelaces," the nurse requested. I did so, and she asked what I had in my pockets. I surrendered my wallet, cell phone, and car keys. I asked the nurse if I could keep the rosary beads that were in my pocket, suspecting that she would say "no" since they're similar to a belt or shoelaces in being useful to harm oneself. But then I relented, remembering what Mike Cutone had said about saying the Memorare instead of the rosary during stressful times. I was relieved that giving up my rosary beads would not make me look like a religious fanatic to the nurse or my daughters. Dee had trained them to watch for religiosity.

As I sat with Bianca on my right side and Dominique to the right of her, we wondered how long this whole process would take before I was admitted to the hospital. To the left of me was Jeffrey, a white Jewish male in his late 30s. A full head of dark black hair, somewhat curly. About my height, five foot eight inches, or maybe a little shorter. He couldn't stop talking. He talked very fast in his Boston accent, and I later learned that he was full-blown manic. Dominique was set off by him from the very beginning, I was a little more patient with him. Jeffrey asked me a lot of questions: "Are these your daughters?" "Yes," I exclaimed, "Bianca is my oldest daughter, 25, and Dominique is 23." "They're beautiful," Jeffrey responded. Bianca has light brown curls with pale blue eyes, about five foot two inches, slender frame. People say she resembles her mother. Dominique looks a little more like me but with brown, long, straight hair and brown eyes, also slender. Also five foot two inches, like all my girls, even Gigi, the youngest. "What are they doing here? Did they come with you?" He could tell that I was the patient by the white wristband that I was now wearing. "Yes, they were concerned about me, so they asked me to meet them here, for an evaluation." "Are you sick? What do you have?" I explained that I have bipolar disorder with psychotic features, and the psych recommended that I stay here. By this time, it was sinking into my brain that I truly was sick, and I needed more than outpatient treatment. Could everyone be wrong?

I asked Jeffrey about himself. Why was he here, and what was his diagnosis? "Well, I'm here because I'm manic and suicidal, but I also have Asperger's!" Something clicked in my head that there was more to him than just bipolar, and his admission about having Asperger's confirmed it. I could tell that Dominique was wondering why I was giving Jeffrey so much attention. She had learned by living in Boston for almost two years to hold back when meeting strangers, and I'm guessing that this guiding rule was doubled in an emergency psych ward. Deep sighs, and sometimes speaking up to Jeffrey that we were just here to help her dad, not to make friends. Jeffrey would quiet down for about two seconds, then start up the conversation again with a million questions.

The Super Bowl was starting, and they introduced the Patriots' players: Tom Brady, Gronk, Sony Michel, Patrick Chung, Trey Flowers; and the Los Angeles Rams. "Who will win? Do the Rams have a chance?" More questions from Jeffrey. Except now the Super Bowl was getting more serious, and Dominique asked him to please be quiet, in a very nice way. But I was beginning to get the hint that asking Jeffrey to be quiet was like asking a dog to give up a juicy bone. Bianca could only laugh—she was smart enough to stay out of it.

I was very kind to Jeffrey because it's just my empathetic nature, and I've had exposure to enough mentally ill people who I knew that couldn't help themselves. But once the opening kick-off commenced, I was also getting more interested in the game. I asked Jeffrey, "Please be quiet, the game has started!" He pointed out that Tom Brady looked ready for this game, quite composed even though it was the Super Bowl. I gave him another request to be quiet, at least during the game. Maybe commercials would be a better time to make observations about the game, even though the Super Bowl has the best commercials of the year. It was hard to follow Jim Nantz and Tony Romo announcing the game. Anyway, you get the hint that it wasn't the most enjoyable Super Bowl I've seen, with Jeffrey bending my ear and Dominique getting more and more upset at his behavior. I was also wondering what Dee, Zach, and Gigi were doing for the Super Bowl. This would be the first Super Bowl that I didn't watch with Dee in 33 years, since we started dating.

Danny was sitting across from us with his mother, not the slightest bit interested in the game, not even facing the large-screen TV. He was more curled up in a ball, not saying a word. His mother was there for him, though, and I couldn't help but feel her pain – I felt fortunate that we were in that psych emergency room for me, not for Bianca or Dominique. All my kids had dodged the bullet of bipolar disorder – all confident, self-assured, and well-adjusted young men and ladies. For crying out loud, two of my daughters were destined for medical school, one was at Babson trying to be a corporate lawyer, and my son vying for a career as an environmentalist. All were doing what they loved, not hindered by mental illness. Danny's mother would get him drinks of water and a blanket, his hair in disarray, and he was looking very depressed. He would leave before Jeffrey and myself, before the Super Bowl was over. I wasn't sure where he was going, and I wondered what my fate would be. Would I be admitted to Mass General, the number two hospital for mental health, or would I be sent to a lesser hospital by an administrator thinking I'd be better off closer to home? You can't help but

Chapter 8

wonder, and the whole thing sounds like a crapshoot.

Meanwhile, the diamond ring that Dee had given me was bothering me more and more, even though I had it blessed twice. Maybe from watching too many Lord of the Rings movies, the thought of disposing of it in the right place was perplexing. After all, the circumstances of me finding the diamond in that strip mall parking lot in 1995 were anything but consoling.

Since Father Bob failed to dispose of it, and now I was sitting in a psych ward emergency room (and I was manic and psychotic); I decided to excuse myself to the men's room, where I simply threw it in the trach container! Not exactly Mount Doom, but I wasn't exactly Frodo Baggins with the One Ring in Lord of the Rings. Case closed, now I'll be fine without that ring on my finger! I wasn't.

The game played on, and to be honest I don't remember all the details of the game. One, because I had other things on my mind; two, because Jeffrey was bending my ear so much that I thought I'd be locked up for assaulting him! I didn't. The game ended 13-3, the New England Patriots over the Los Angeles Rams. At least something to be happy about.

Another patient entered the room being escorted by two large, burly aides. I never learned his name, but you could tell by his wild eyes that he was in trouble. You don't want to look a patient like this in the eyes because, basically, you don't want any contact with them at all. Tall and thin, he sat across from us to the right and wasn't interested in the TV. One of the aides never left his side. Immediately, you could feel the tension in the room. His eyes darted around the room. I had been in similar situations before in psych emergency rooms, but never with my two daughters; or anyone else that I loved, for that matter. It was inevitable that we would lock eyes, and he made a motion towards me; but he didn't get very far before the aide grabbed his arm, signaling him to hold back. Shortly after that, the other aide entered the room, and the two of them escorted him back out of the ward. Everyone was relieved. I don't know where he was taken, or what would ever happen to this man, but once again I couldn't help the sad feeling in the pit of my stomach that he had a long road ahead of him. Sometimes there's a fine line between the psych emergency room and the jail, and this was one of those cases.

The doctor finally came into the room: "Domenic? Domenic Zarrella?" "Yes, that's me," I quipped. He approached me and informed me that I would be staying in the ward that night, pointing toward a mobile bed on wheels in the hallway. "Where am I going from here," I retorted. "We're not sure, we haven't made those arrangements yet. We'll know in the morning." More uncertainty. At this point, Dominique asked the doctor if she could take a break and leave the ward to get some refreshments for herself, and the doctor escorted her out of the room. She was locked in as I was. Bianca would stay with me until Dominique returned, then she would leave for a respite for herself. Of course, I wasn't allowed to leave.

Later that night, Jeffrey would also leave Mass General, relieved that he would be going to McLean Hospital in Belmont, Massachusetts. He didn't have to sleep here. We said our goodbyes – Bianca was still out of the room. I was still feeling safe and relieved to be in that ward instead of being out on my own, sick and moving from place to place for a night here, a week there. Surrender. I was more relieved than anxious. I was given a jonnie to change into, and I went to the same restroom that I disposed of the ring in to change. Coming back out, an aide directed me to the bed. It must have been about midnight. I remember nothing after that, until arriving at McLean Hospital the next day. I only remember having a nightmare that I was driving around in the Milan with no place to sleep and being pulled over by the police, who inspected my car; they could tell that I was practically homeless. My big fear of being discovered as being on-the-run came true in this dream. Dominique and Bianca said their goodnights at 2 a.m.; off to their apartments. I also don't remember them saying "Good night," to me and assuring me that they would come back to visit me in the morning, as they had to work, being Monday. But many days later, Dominique told me that I was sound asleep when they left but woke up to tell them I loved them. I still don't know if they gave me a sedative that night or if I was just worn out.

But during the whole time of the Super Bowl, I was texting my friends.

"H" is Mike, and he lives in Boise ("H" is for Headly because he has a large head). "Bells" is Mike, "Moody" is Mike, "Huck" is Mike (he doesn't have a cell phone), "Mario" is Mario, and "Chris" is Chris. They didn't know that I was at Mass General at this point. One of the texts goes like this.

Feb 3, 10:21 p.m. by Domenic

Chris, a friend of mine told me the story of years ago when you guys were neighbors. He got a dog to walk for exercise. You drove by and commented that he looked good, and he responded by saying he lost 20 pounds walking the dog. You recommended that he get two more dogs. (:

From Left: **H., Louise (Steve's girlfriend), Steve, Moody, Bells and Mario**

The next thing I remember is being at McLean Hospital in Belmont and seeing Jeffrey in the cafeteria as they toured me around after admitting me. He was thrilled to see me again. "Hey look, it's my friend Domenic from Mass General! We spent last night together watching the Super Bowl with his two daughters. Can you believe that we ended up at the same hospital?" I don't remember waking up that Monday morning after the Super Bowl or getting the news that I was going to McLean, or even whether I saw Bianca and Dominique that morning. I can only guess that, in the ambulance ride between Mass General and McLean, they offered me a sedative to assure that I'd be calm for the ride, and it wiped out my memory banks. The only reason that I even knew how I got to McLean is that I got the ambulance bill weeks later. The only other time I felt like that – complete loss of short-term memory – was after the ambulance

Chapter 8

ride during my first nervous breakdown in 1995, after which I had that conversation with the doctor who asked if I knew what I had said when I was admitted. I'm not sure what drug they used, but I didn't protest because I was safe. I was glad to have been shipped to McLean, the #1 hospital in the world for mental health. And I remember the conversation I had the night before in Mass General, where Dominique said, "Dad, wherever you end up tonight, you should get your outpatient treatment here at Mass General." The thoughts going through my head now were – "I'm being treated by the #1 and #2 hospitals in the world for mental health – McLean and Mass General. How blessed am I?"

McLean is an old hospital, founded by the Massachusetts Legislature in 1811 as part of the Massachusetts General Hospital; intended to provide both physical and mental health treatment. Although my ward was in an older building, it was modernized and well maintained. Newer large metal windows, ornate oak woodwork, pastel-colored walls, and well lit, it would be my home until further notice. Of course, at the time I didn't know how long my stay would be. I was shown to my room at the end of the hall. The layout of the ward was like an "H," with the cafeteria and nurse's station in the middle of the "H," patient rooms, conference rooms, and group meeting rooms in the other sections. My room was very plain with two simple, single beds, two closets, and one desk. Light tan in color, and the ceilings were expansive. Nothing on the walls. Danny from Mass General was my roommate. He entered the room, and it was obvious that he was still quite depressed. The counselor introduced us, and we shook hands. I could see in his young eyes the pain of someone struggling to make sense of his young life – he was only in his early 20s. A couple days later, his mother would bring his guitar, and he would play it when I wasn't in the room, out of respect for me. I learned that he enjoyed skateboarding, mountain biking, and playing his guitar when he was feeling well enough to do those things.

I never got to know Danny very well, except that he was a polite and sensitive young man, like many of the depressed patients that I've encountered. Aside from the manic/psychotic individuals that I've come across who are borderline violent, most people with depression are quite reserved. They've turned the anger inward (Freud said that depression is anger turned inward). And obviously mania is anger turned outward. But why all this anger? What could cause such violence inside a person? My guess is that, aside from the genetics of it all, finding one's purpose in life can be very confusing in the modern age, especially. Also, the issue of control – by a parent, spouse, or friend contributes. Adolescence is especially a time of rebellion against parents and society at large – I think because the child knows that he/she is destined for failure on the path they're currently on. Yet they either don't know how to express themselves, or they have a controlling parent who only wants the best for their child but is being too oppressive in how they go about it. The harder you force a square peg into a round hole, the harder the opposition. "Go to college," "Be an accountant," "Take over the family business," "Play a sport," "Why would you want to do otherwise?"

In a culture where dominance is the key to success, and Type A is celebrated – especially in some fields – a more sensitive person can be left behind and bewildered. Failure is not your friend in the career arena, and that's what you feel like – a failure. Albert Einstein was quoted as saying, "Everyone is a genius, but if you judge a fish by its ability to climb a tree, it will live its whole life believing that it is stupid." Depression and anxiety go hand-in-hand. Depression is the result of peering into the future expecting the worst or the result of stuffing our emotions. Anxiety is fear more in the present. I know them well. Some of these problems are situational, like an adolescent trying to find themselves. Some of them are genetic. I believe that for a person who truly has bipolar disorder there is a genetic portion, and medicine is required. I've also heard that mania is simply depression spun out of control. Some people mask their depression with hyper-activity, so they don't need to confront their feelings. Alcohol is also an acceptable outlet for depression in our culture, unless it gets totally out of hand. It's also a respite for the chronically depressed because, for at least a few hours, you feel okay, when for the rest of 24/7/365 life is torturous. It's called self-medicating. Stress is a huge factor adding to the potion. Stressors are different for different people. What stresses you out might be enjoyable to me.

In my history, I believe that the stress of obtaining a bachelor's degree in electrical engineering was too much for me. I was the one who wanted to achieve it, not my parents, and I wanted to get it done in four years. After two years of school, the anxiety started to get to me. Depression followed. I wasn't doing well with my 2.3 GPA, and my father actually suggested, "Domenic, did you ever think of majoring in business?" after my sophomore year. Upon graduation, with all the uncertainty of the future – should I get married to the girl I've been dating for five years? Did I choose the right career? Where will I live, even what state shall I live in? That's when I had my first major depression, right after graduation. I had a job all lined up at Raytheon in Waltham, Massachusetts, but the four years of stress hit me like a ton of bricks. Of course, I didn't know it was depression because it wasn't discussed in my family. All that fatigue was new to me, and I thought it was physical, a virus like mono, or something like that. But doctors couldn't find anything. Having the bipolar gene combined with the stress was the cause, though. I self-medicated with alcohol for 12 years until, in 1995 at age 34, I had that conflict with my bosses that led me to my first hospitalization. In the meantime, I had met and married Dee, and we had our first two children. During all this time, I performed well in my career, progressing from engineer to senior engineer to principal engineer at Digital Equipment Corporation before going into sales. At Digital, I was helping develop the computer memories (semiconductor "chips") that are used with CPUs in all types of computers, like cell phones.

I had the impression that Danny was going through similar tribulations. Working for a landscaping company may not have been his ideal goal, but where did he fit in? I felt sorry for such a sweet, sweet kid, but all I could do was be reassuring. Plus, obviously I had my own issues to deal with. He helped me, too, by displaying the kindness that I felt was left behind by many in our culture.

That night, my first night, I was invited to a group session on communication. Then a group wrap-up meeting where you discuss your accomplishments for the day and challenges for the next day. The schedule in a psych ward is very full, but you can opt out of a meeting if you're not feeling up to it. Of course, your counselor and psychiatrist would remind you of your attendance because they kept a record of which sessions you attended and which ones you didn't. Attendance helped determine how soon you'd be released.

I didn't sleep well that first night, wondering how long they would keep me there, and trying too hard to sleep because the staff monitored your sleep. About every 30 minutes or so, they would slip the door open a crack and peak into the room to check on the two patients in the room. The bright fluorescent hallway lights gave them plenty of vision into the room. If you got up before 6 a.m., they would send you back to bed, but at 6:30 a.m., you could shower and begin your day. At 7 a.m., the staff shift changed, so you couldn't shave then because a staff member had to give you a razor from the stockroom and watch you shave, then take the razor back, and discard it. After showering, the nursing staff would take your blood pressure, temperature, and pulse, and ask you how you slept. Of course, they saw the notes from the night staff about how you slept, anyway, but just checking to see if everything lined up. My blood pressure gets really high when I'm anxious in the hospital – as high as 159/98. I'm normally borderline at 138/84, but my blood pressure was always a concern to the nurses and doctors. I guess they didn't want me to have a stroke under their care.

After vitals came breakfast at 8 a.m. Ernest from the cafeteria staff would wheel his cart down the hall and into the cafeteria, which was bright and sunny. The unit had only about 25 patients, so the cafeteria wasn't that big, maybe the size of four large conference rooms. Ernest would always greet the patients as they stepped up to the cart for their turn for food. The food was tasty, and there were always a few choices – pancakes, waffles, scrambled eggs, or cereal. Oatmeal was always available as a side dish for breakfast. "Welcome to my world!!" he would always say; and after a few days, I was comfortable enough to greet him with "Welcome to my planet!!" Ernest was always cheerful, and if a patient was feeling down (which many were), he would attempt to transfer his energy to that person. I think Ernest was actually part of the psych ward staff, reporting what he saw in the cafeteria to the counselors. Upon finishing your meal, you could always count on Ernest to pick up your plate and bring it to the waste basket. But first, he would always act like a magician, distracting you by pointing out the window and saying "Look at that bird," or something like that. Then he would steal your plate away while you weren't looking or secretly place an apple on the table in front of you. He got me every time!

Shortly after breakfast was the first counseling session, at about 9 a.m.. There was a whiteboard on the wall outside the nurses' station with the schedule for the day. Broken into two groups, sometimes there were sessions common to both groups, but mostly they were separated. Like Newton-Wellesley, there was another unit for more seriously ill patients; but unlike Newton-Wellesley, it wasn't connected to my ward. McLean has a large campus of many gray stone buildings with separate buildings for addiction, long-term, and short-term care, like the unit I was in. Also unlike Newton-Wellesley, cell phones were allowed in the unit! This is unusual because the staff didn't want the patient to place disturbing calls to the person or people they had conflict with before being admitted. But they allowed cell phones anyway. Thank God, because my cell phone would soon become my life-support system to the outside world, mainly my tight circle of friends; Mike, Mike, Mike, and Mike, and Mario!

Chapter 8

We added Chris to the mix of knuckleheads just before my admission. All of us are high school buddies.

CHAPTER 9

LEARNING NEW TRICKS

S hortly after getting settled into the ward, I discovered something enlightening. I was always in search of the missing clue that would "crack the code" to the emotional side of my illness. So I would read all the corkboards on the walls in the halls of the ward, and in the outside world, maybe books, homilies, speeches, and yes, the Bible – maybe something could help me understand. On this particular day there was an 8-and-a-half by 11 laminated sheet on the wall with the title "McLean Hospital Spirituality & Mental Health Program." It described one of their meditation counseling sessions on forgiveness. One of the bullets on this sheet read "Empathize – try to identify a plausible reason for the other's actions". This intrigued me for two reasons: 1) I retract from conflict because I'm uncomfortable with it. The bad news for me is that I'm very often in a conflict situation, especially in sales. And 2) I do have a big, empathetic heart. The advice in the counseling session described how some people are abrasive or aggressive when trying to meet a certain need, many times good and true needs; but they just try to achieve it with the wrong strategy. And since aggression met with aggression usually escalates, a more effective approach is recommended. Maybe the biblical term is "Love your Enemy," which I never could understand, none-the-less put into practice. But think about it: especially with someone you do love, like a spouse or one of your children, trying to understand what emotions they're really trying to relay instead of attacking back at them might avoid much heartache. "Help me understand?" is the practical advice for this situation. Don't be surprised if the person you're interacting with can't elaborate on what's bothering them. Also, some people who do true harm believe that what they're doing is actually in pursuit of something good, like fighting against an ideology they think is evil.

I never got to put it in practice with Dee because our adversarial relationship had gone too far, but I hoped for the opportunity in the future. Regardless, this strategy disarmed me. I felt more at peace with the inner conflicts that I myself was facing; and therefore, this feeling was brand new to me and gave me hope that my individual interpersonal style could be used to my advantage. If I could learn to work with the Type-A, aggressive people that I normally resented, it would open up a whole new world to me, a world that is beyond imagination. It fit in well with my Christian training.

But beyond this simple one-page laminated sheet on the wall of McLean, I would discover that the Spirituality and Mental

Health Program included other faith-based initiatives, with one aspect enlisting Old Testament and New Testament Bible verses to contemplate. The Qur'an and other non-Christian sources are also used. And I might have been part of the study that helped realize this program. In 2011, I reached out to McLean for treatment of my major depression, and being a new patient to them I was assigned to a young resident counselor who was investigating faith-based psychological treatment, David Rosmarin. I also had a psychiatrist on my team. At the time, David Rosmarin's treatment was groundbreaking, and I'm sure that he wrote his doctoral thesis on his theory that employing faith in a mental health program would be beneficial. After about a year of unsuccessful treatment at McLean, however, I turned to Pat Senior at Island Counseling in Worcester in 2011. But when I asked Cindy, the meditation counselor who ran the Forgiveness session, how this faith-based program came about, she mentioned David Rosmarin's name, the counselor that I had worked with nine years prior.

I walked into the cafeteria on the second morning, and there was a commotion. A large young man, about six-foot two inches tall and 260 pounds, with a couple days' worth of dark nubby facial hair, was surrounded by three of the hospital staff, and he was angry. One of the counselors very calmly tried to settle him, but it wasn't effective as he grew more and more restless. My walking into the room at that time placed me directly in the path of this impending storm, and he looked at me glaringly and asked why I thought it was my business to butt in on their conversation? I was startled, but not surprised, as another counselor explained that I wasn't involved in the altercation, so to leave me out of it. Thank God he listened to her because I was in no mood to argue. But I knew this wouldn't be my last interface with Michael. I knew his name because the staff members had repeated it so many times while I was in that room. I very wisely turned my back and high-tailed it out of that cafeteria.

If you're wondering what a group counseling session in a mental ward is like, don't worry, I have lots of experience and I'll explain it to you. Most groups are smaller in order to keep the conversations intimate; about eight to 10 people, more or less, except for morning call meetings and nightly wrap-up. Then the whole ward is invited. But about a quarter of the patients don't show up because they're too depressed or psychotic.

First, the counselors introduce themselves. Mostly young students, I'm guessing, who are putting in the required hours of experience to obtain a graduate degree in psychology. Some are more experienced in their years – read older – and have a lot of wisdom to offer being that they've dealt with a lot of sick patients over the years; and are still working, which shows their perseverance in such a tough field. Each counselor also has a responsibility as one-on-one counselors for five or six individual patients. Next comes introduction of the patients, going around the room in a large circle. Some are showered and dressed. Some are still in their pajamas (you've never seen such variety in pajamas) and haven't showered. Some are excited to be there, some don't speak at all, wrapped up in a severe depression like I've never experienced before. These are the ones that I feel most sad for! As for me, being moderately hypo-manic, I was never shy about sharing my experiences. As a matter of fact, I sometimes guessed that I was sharing too much and not giving the other patients an opportunity to speak. But the counselors reassured me that my input was very valuable: "Domenic, you have good insight into your illness!" More than one counselor also pointed out to me that, being conscious of my many words in the sessions, that I was very polite in offering to step back and give the other people an opportunity to give their input. I guess they'd rather have me blabbing away than having a quiet room.

The counselors were experienced in directing the conversation and cutting someone off – in a very kind way – if they were complaining too much about the conditions in the ward, their psychiatrist, or their archenemy on the outside (usually a parent, spouse, or boss). Each counselor had their own individual personality and, therefore, their own personal style. Patients were also allowed to comment on another patient's dilemma, which was very helpful because they were largely in the same boat. Many times, their perspective gave new hope to the person on the receiving end of their advice, and individual experience with a certain type of med was invaluable information. All of the one-on-one counselors were on the day shift, and they checked in with you for a five- or 10-minute conversation randomly throughout the day, once a day: "Domenic, do you have a few minutes to talk?" My one-on-one counselor was Haley. I'm guessing she was about 23 and she was DDG – drop dead gorgeous. Blonde straight shiny hair, big brown eyes, about five-foot four inches tall, and thin. She was a natural beauty, not much make-up, and very compassionate. Maybe I would want to extend my visit?? But I looked at her as more of a daughter. Fifty-seven years old, salt-and-pepper hair (more salt than pepper these days), light brown eyes, a little chubby (I blame it on the meds), I feel confident but not overly vain. Haley was always intent at getting the temperature inside my head, mostly asking me questions about how I felt that day. My feelings would lead her to the intensity of my illness: Was I overly angry? Self-absorbed? Sad? Anxious? Anxious was too general a term for her, as she wanted more details than that about specifically what was going on with my emotions. Having been married for 28 years and being a family man, I guess my crystal ball was mostly aimed at my marriage and how my young-adult children felt about the potential divorce of their parents. Remember, anxiety is fear in the present. My anxiety was less intense this time, however, because our youngest child, Gigi, was off to college. No coincidence, because I had waited until she was grown to address the problems in the marriage – not uncommon. Unlike the anxiety I would have at the potential of breaking up a family with young children. Plus, I had reapplied for, and been accepted on, Social Security Disability. So, with that and part-time substitute teaching, I knew that I could support myself. Not everyone on Social Security Disability could do that because not everyone's check was as big as mine (big might be the wrong word, sufficient might be better).

It was soon after my second day that I would inevitably end up with Jeffrey from Mass General in my group. I believe it was on meditation. There were a lot of sessions on different styles of meditation – Eastern, visual, sensory, auditory, guided, physical head-to-toe relaxation – all to quiet the unquiet mind. But anyway, when we circled the room for introductions, Jeffrey was quick to introduce himself as "Domenic's friend." Remember, Jeffrey is on the Asperger's spectrum, and he was sky-high manic on entering the hospital, as I was. He went on to explain how we met in that Mass General emergency room, and that I was with my two young daughters watching the New England Patriots win the Super Bowl. He would admit being very manic and talkative during that Super Bowl, and pointed out that "Domenic would continually ask me to "shut up!" which I never said to him. But I guess that's how it felt coming into his ears. This is a theme that Jeffrey would repeat in many sessions to come; how Domenic told him to "shut up" during the Super Bowl!

It was also inevitable that I would run into Michael. But I wasn't lucky enough to have the encounter be in a group counseling session, but in the cafeteria again. This time, I was in the cafeteria as Michael walked in. Sitting at a table with three other patients, I was just going about my business when Michael saw me, remembering my pretty face from the previous day. I immediately tensed up. But knowing that if I didn't want him to be a continual source of agita during my stay at McLean, I would have to confront him if he wanted to engage. And he did. "Hey, it's the wise-guy who walked in on me and the counselors yesterday and got me into trouble!" There was no denying that it was me he was directing his comment to, so I got up from my seat and approached him in an unthreatening way. This took a lot of guts because remember, Michael's stature was that of a TD Garden (the former Boston Garden sports complex) security guard. No match for me! I calmly explained to him; "Michael, I remember you from the other day, and yes, I got you into trouble. But I meant no harm, and I could tell that the counselors were concerned about you getting out of hand. I also could tell that you probably were angry about a valid topic, and you never intended to harm anyone, including me." He acknowledged my intentions, and I could quickly tell that he was softening his stance. So I bravely continued, "You're an intimidating figure, but I can tell that you're just a big teddy bear trying to be understood in a bad situation." His eyes became like the abominable snowman in Rudolf the Red-Nosed Reindeer – large and somewhat guilty as he sheepishly glanced at me – and he could feel my empathy for his situation. I had an immediate friend!

Michael wasn't done, however; and he introduced himself as Michael the Archangel, and that he had legions of angels that would now protect me. I couldn't believe the change in this young man, because he truly was now the gentlest person in the whole ward. But I was truly genuine with Michael in my actions and emotions, and I think he could sense it. My first effort at employing empathy in a conflict situation was a huge success! This approach is a lot easier with a stranger than with someone you have a long-broken relationship with. Strict battle lines of conflict have weakened the trust in those cases.

Having had enough experiences with people in Michael's state of mind, I knew that he was fully psychotic in thinking he was the Archangel Michael. And in this case, I also knew that his condition was more permanent, not just a passing fad in his imagination. Maybe his condition was medicine resistant? Actually, it probably was medicine resistant.

Since we were in the same ward for six or seven days, Michael and I would see each other frequently, mostly in the cafeteria. He would always engage now when he saw me. "Domenic, I can feel a legion of angels surrounding us and protecting us here! Do you believe me?" I would always agree with him because I do believe in St. Michael the Archangel, and I do pray to him often. "Yes, Michael, I do believe that angels are protecting us here!" He would continue about what those angels were doing and saying to him, and I would get a little too uncomfortable with the conversation because I didn't want to let Michael to go too far. Sometimes I would be expecting the staff to intervene in our galactic conversations, but they never did. The staff had a station outside the café where they would hang out if they weren't in a counseling session. One or two of them would always be there, and they could break up conversations that went on in the café if needed.

I had trouble sleeping for most of my stay at McLean partly because of the uncertainty over when I would be released, or sometimes even if I'd be released. My psychiatrist, Dr. Solomon, prescribed valium as needed to help me sleep, but I would resist this solution as much as possible because of its addictive nature. But it quickly worked like a charm for anxiety, so you really had to weigh its use. The doctors really want you to sleep well. One night, I woke up around 3 a.m. and couldn't fall back to sleep after wrestling around for an hour. Of course, I always pretended to be sleeping when I heard the staff walking down the hall toward me. But shortly after, I got up and wandered to the nurses' station to inform them that I couldn't sleep – the pharmacy was open 24/7 – so I asked for some meds to help me. The white colored vinyl floor tiles in the hallway gave an antiseptic feel, and the fluorescent lights didn't help that hallway from feeling cold and unwelcoming. But I didn't expect the Crowne Plaza Hotel, so I never complained. Most nights, the hallway was very quiet when I would walk to the nurses' station or the bathroom. On this particular night, maybe seeing my resistance to taking the valium, the nurse asked if I'd like to try Benadryl instead, and it worked. What a relief! I didn't need it every night, but I knew that I could fall back on it if needed. My chart was altered to reflect this.

Chapter 9

I saw Dr. Solomon every weekday, and the attending psychiatrist on weekends. I was lucky to have him assigned to me because he's very bright – one of the number one doctors in the number one hospital for psychiatric care – and it showed. He was a bit of a wise guy since he was very intuitive, and after a couple days he could shoot bullets into your story if you weren't careful. As I mentioned previously, when I complained about Dee not listening to me about my concerns for over a decade, he asked if I had ever not listened to her? Of course, I hadn't. Maybe that's a clue that I overlooked? On another occasion, I shared with him that Dee was talking to the social worker about divorcing me, and he quipped "That's what you want, isn't it?" It made me think about whether I really wanted a divorce. It seems that my arrows usually came flying back at me like a boomerang when talking to Dr. Solomon! Dr. Solomon never said these things in an uncharitable way, it's just that he was more like a lawyer than a doctor in breaking your story apart. I could tell that he was kind and caring by his interactions with patients in the hallways. He always welcomed their encounters but kept them brief because he was only on the ward for short periods of time. When Michael was discharged, Dr. Solomon gave him a big hug. No one complained about him in the group sessions or in the café.

During this time, I took Mike Cutone's advice and said the Memorare daily instead of the rosary. I would also visit the sensory room every evening to listen to music on headphones supplied by the ward. The sensory room is somewhat soundproofed, so if you weren't wearing headphones the music wouldn't be too loud outside the room. I mostly listened to the Hootie and the Blowfish "Cracked Rear View" album from the 1990s, the era when I had my first nervous breakdown. My favorite song is "Hold my Hand." At the time, I took that song to mean that Jesus was holding my hand through the tough times:

Hold My Hand

With a little love and some tenderness

We'll walk upon the water

We'll rise above the mess

With a little peace and some harmony

We'll take the world together

We'll take them by the hand

'Cause I've got a hand for you, oh

'Cause I wanna run with you

Yesterday, I saw you standing there

Your head was down, your eyes were red

No comb had touched your hair

I said, get up, and let me see you smile

We'll take a walk together

Walk the road awhile, 'cause

'Cause I've got a hand for you

I've got a hand for you

Chapter 9

'Cause I wanna run with you

Won't you let me run with you, yeah

Want you to hold my hand

(Hold my hand)

I'll take you to a place

Where you can be

(Hold my hand)

Anything you wanna be because

I wanna love you the best that

The best that I can

See I was wasted, and I was wasting time

'Til I thought about your problems

I thought about your crimes

Then I stood up, and then I screamed aloud

I don't wanna be part of your problems

Don't wanna be part of your crowd, no

'Cause I've got a hand for you

I've got a hand for you

'Cause I wanna run with you

Won't you let me run with you

Want you to hold my hand

(Hold my hand)

I'll take you to the promised land

(Hold my hand)

Maybe we can't change the world but

I wanna love you the best that

The best that I can, yeah

Let me walk, oh won't you let me, let me

(Hold my hand)

Want you to hold my hand

(Hold my hand)

I'll take you to a place where you can be

(Hold my hand)

Anything you wanna be because

I oh no, no, no, no, no

(Hold my hand)

Want you to hold my hand

(Hold my hand)

I'll take you to the promised land

(Hold my hand)

Chapter 9

Maybe we can't change the world but

I wanna love you the best that

The best that I can

Oh, best that I can

Source: LyricFind

Songwriters: Darius Rucker / Dean Felber /

Jim Sonefeld / Mark Bryan

Hold My Hand lyrics © Sony/ATV Music Publishing LLC

Below is the Bible verse that the song refers to, about "walking upon the water." It reminds me of the many times I've taken a risk (trying to walk on water towards Jesus) and let fear overcome me (falling into the water). But Jesus grabbed my hand.

Jesus Walks on the Sea

22 Immediately Jesus [a]made His disciples get into the boat and go before Him to the other side, while He sent the multitudes away. 23 And when He had sent the multitudes away, He went up on the mountain by Himself to pray. Now when evening came, He was alone there. 24 But the boat was now [b]in the middle of the sea, tossed by the waves, for the wind was contrary.

25 Now in the fourth watch of the night Jesus went to them, walking on the sea. 26 And when the disciples saw Him walking on the sea, they were troubled, saying, "It is a ghost!" And they cried out for fear.

27 But immediately Jesus spoke to them, saying, [c]"Be of good cheer! [d]It is I; do not be afraid."

28 And Peter answered Him and said, "Lord, if it is You, command me to come to You on the water."

29 So He said, "Come." And when Peter had come down out of the boat, he walked on the water to go to Jesus. 30 But when he saw [e]that the wind was boisterous, he was afraid; and beginning to sink he cried out, saying, "Lord, save me!"

31 And immediately Jesus stretched out His hand and caught him, and said to him, "O you of little faith, why did you doubt?" 32 And when they got into the boat, the wind ceased.

33 Then those who were in the boat [f]came and worshiped Him, saying, "Truly You are the Son of God" (Matthew 14:22-33 NKJV)

This verse is what inspired me to name our boat "Walking on Water."

As I got to meet more and more patients, another complex patient entered the story. Casey was in her mid-20s, short in stature, with shoulder-length red hair and a strong Boston accent. From Southie, she was here for major depression – but you'd never know it from talking to her! She always had something to say, unlike most of the depressed patients, and after a few days she couldn't take the pain anymore, so her team decided to administer ECT (shock therapy) in an attempt to free her from this menace in her life. She was very fond of her five-year-old son and her "Grampy," her grandfather on her mother's side. Grampy would come to visit her daily from his house in Southie. I loved talking to Casey because of her sassy attitude and slightly sarcastic sense of humor. Again, very uncommon for a patient of ECT. But we made light of our situation, and Jeffrey sometimes palled around with us on our escorted visits to the hospital cafeteria. You had to be cleared to be allowed to go to the on-campus cafeteria with the staff.

Richard was an older Asian man who sat next to me in one of the group sessions. He didn't say a word and rarely opened his eyes, too fatigued and lethargic from the major depression that inflicted him. I wondered how he got to the session. The group counselor would try to engage him in conversation to no avail – not a word. As the days advanced, and as Richard received his ECT treatments, he began to be a little more interactive. I learned that he was a pharmacist who recently retired early because of his illness. With his children grown, and his career in its' twilight, he lost his purpose in life.

John seemed to have no apparent reason for being depressed. A financial analyst in his mid-40s and with a wife and two kids, he had a successful career. In group, he was able to rewind the events of his life; but there were no real clues as to why he was here, aside from the fact that he was so depressed that he had climbed to the top of a cell phone tower, intending to jump off. "All I had to do was let go…" But for some reason, he relented.

Bianca and Dominique would ride their bikes from Boston

to Belmont, about 15 miles, to visit me and bring me clothes, treats, and other items. Remember, this was early/mid-February in Boston – it was a cold ride. But they mostly came on the milder days, after work at Mass General. Sometimes Dee would meet them at McLean, and they would all visit with me. On one particular visit, the four of us went to the on-campus cafeteria to grab some coffee or juice. You needed further clearance to leave the ward with family members, without the staff. I was sitting across from Dee discussing my illness and the latest info on the meds and counseling. That's when she noticed that my diamond ring wasn't on my finger. "Where's your ring?" pointing to my hand. "Oh, I never saw it again after they took my belongings away from me at Mass General." Of course, I never saw it again because I had dumped it in the trash of that men's room! Dee was always interested in how the new meds were working and for some reason wanted me to get back on lithium instead of Lamictal, and I'm sure she voiced this opinion to the social worker many times. But Dr. Solomon never waivered.

On the third day, Dr. Solomon had some good news: "Domenic, there's a drug that I'd like you to consider. It's called Invega and is a cousin to Risperdal. But it's a second generation anti-psychotic that has fewer side effects. Because of the lower side effects, we can give you a higher effective dose of it." He explained that, while Risperdal was very effective for me, it wasn't strong enough of a dose to get me through the rocky, psychotic experiences. A higher dose of Risperdal would have too many side effects. He explained it as synonymous to a boat riding on water with rocks slightly below it. If the rocks got too close to the surface – meaning that if my level of psychosis got too close to the level of the Risperdal, there could be consequences. But if we doubled the effective dose using Invega, there would be more margin and, therefore, less likelihood of my symptoms becoming problematic. I agreed to this med change immediately, and Dr. Solomon got up and shook my hand, then left the conference room. The pharmacist later explained to me that Invega was developed in the lab by simulating the brain's receptors responsible for psychosis into a computer model. Large computer memories would then take the molecules in Risperdal and fire them at the receptors, only keeping those that affected the psychosis receptors. They would then remove the molecules that didn't affect psychosis because those are the ones that affect the weight gain and brain fog receptors. At higher doses some tiredness would remain, as I found out later, because just as Invega slows down your thinking, it also slows down your metabolism. And, like Risperdal, other side effects like elevated glucose and cholesterol remained. I guess they hadn't perfected their computer models. But what a miracle! Months later my dose was lowered, and the tiredness abated. This was also very interesting to me because I had helped develop those computer main memories, being an expert in the semiconductors that comprise them. Unlike switching other meds, converting from Risperdal to Invega was immediate because of their similarities. It was done in a day. Converting from lithium to Lamictal takes longer because of the effects of weaning off one med and ramping up the other. Lamictal, especially, has to be increased over time because of a potential skin rash that could be dangerous. You can't just start the desired dose right off the bat.

Also on the third day, my team advised me that I should work on my self-esteem during this stint in the hospital. It seems that a majority of people suffering from depression have self-esteem problems at their root. Group sessions would investigate what kind of hobbies or activities the patient liked or was good at to remind them of their capabilities. My one-on-one counselor, Haley, now had something to focus on in my recuperation.

By the fourth day, I started to get more comfortable at McLean because I felt safe in the ward, and because I trusted my doctor and the team assigned to me. The social worker would also sit with me every other day, and since she was also talking to Dee on the phone, I could sense what Dee was telling her. Dee was saying that she didn't feel safe with me and wanted me to be medicated enough to keep me from acting the way I did. Lithium. But as I explained to my team, it was because I had gone off my meds out of desperation, not because they weren't strong enough, that I acted that way. If Dee was listening to me, this wouldn't have happened. It took until about the eighth or ninth day that I felt my team was believing me, and the argument started to slant in my direction.

But in the meantime, I attended almost every counseling session available to me. One of the sessions was crafts or art. The thinking goes that if you can't get out of your own head, i.e. your thoughts are all-encompassing, working with your hands would require that your mind was engaged in the activity instead of being off in the distance. With psychiatric patients in general, this is the problem; not living in the present, but living either in the past or the future. In that 50-minutes, we made everything from bracelets for our family members to sand scenes made out of plastic trees, boats, and people, like a beach scene. The sand kept the sensory faculties working – distracting the brain.

Communication, conflict, personal hygiene, meds, sleep

practices (how to sleep better), career development, and services available to us on the outside, like housing, were other session topics. The schedule of sessions for the day was always posted on the whiteboard in the hall when you got up in the morning. Gym time to play basketball, time in the workout room to lift weights, or a walk outside comprised the daily physical activities.

Dr. Solomon, the social worker, and I discussed discharge on about the eighth day, after I posed the question. One of Dr. Solomon's comments was that it was too early for discharge because I was still hypomanic. "Domenic, the staff is noting that you smile a lot, indicative of hypomania." At the end of a subsequent meeting, Dr. Solomon again highlighted that the staff were noticing that I smiled a lot, and upon leaving the room at the end of the meeting I said, "Dr. Solomon, if you keep me here until I stop smiling, I'm going to be here a long time." (In other words, I smile a lot regardless of whether I'm hypomanic or not). He answered, "I know, Domenic, I know."

I enjoyed Ernest's joyful attitude and looked forward to encountering him at every breakfast and lunch. Ernest was from Haiti, black, almost six feet tall, and thin, with a wiry grey beard and a full head of short curly hair. On this particular day, upon presenting me with my scrambled eggs and oatmeal, he told me an old Haitian folk tale that was passed down to him. "A witch can put two kinds of spells on you with fire. Both are synonymous with the fall leaves on trees. One leaf is deep red because the spell sucks the blood (and life) life out of you, leaving you drained. The other is bright yellow, because it burns life's impurities out of you, leaving you fresh and renewed." Ernest asked that if I'd like to learn more about this parable, he would bring some information for me the next day. Now, witches and I don't get along very well, as I explained earlier in the book about Julia, so I was afraid to get involved. But trying more to be more open-minded and less fearful and superstitious, I agreed to Ernest's proposal. The next day and no information. On the third day, he said he had the folk tale that he promised me. He presented me with a white 8 ½' x 11" piece of paper with bold black print. Now, I'm still a little weary of this whole idea and am now wondering the reason why Ernest was always so friendly – was it just to pass on his witchcraft? But something told me that he was genuine, and there was no harm in his friendly offer. When I read the paper later in my room, I was surprised to read that the folk tale was nothing about fire or trees or fall leaves, but about an elusive character roaming the streets of Boston. Ernest had written this short essay set just before Christmas when the police were notified of a strange phenomenon.

You can imagine that I was relieved to find that Ernest's tale was nothing about witchcraft and everything about youthful innocence. The next day I asked Ernest if I could reprint his story in my book and he agreed, so here it is in its' original form:

News from Boston

Shortly after Thanksgiving, one day, early in the morning, residents in the Back Bay area made 911 calls. Some reported that they heard an unfamiliar noise similar to a heavy stump passing into the neighborhood. Others felt their houses were trembling. A large number of callers heard a loud bang. When agents of the Boston Police Department arrived at the corner of Huntington Avenue and Belvedere Street, in front of the Cheesecake Factory, there was a gigantic golden ball and a tiny red ball. The balls were both Christmas ornaments in shapes and colors. The oversized golden ball was taller than a person, about eight feet high. The red ball, on the other hand, was much smaller, about one inch in diameter. After a well-conducted investigation, the detectives discovered that it was Big Foot. While carrying his Christmas decoration, the ball fell right there. To everyone's surprise, the investigators discovered something about Big Foot that no one thought was possible. He has a friend. Who it turns out to be Mini Foot. The facts that lead to such conclusions are: the presence of the one-inch small red ball, the tiny footprints going to the same direction as those of the big footprints, and many other facts that were not disclosed. In summary, from the Boston Police Headquarters in a press conference on this big event in our historic city of Boston, it is known that Big Foot is living in one of the tunnels in Boston. On the subject, Mini Foot, the elusiveness of such a personality never before known to human being until now, and the very little evidence he left behind, made it extremely hard to know his whereabout.

Ernest Laroche

As with every stay in a psychiatric ward, the patient can't be released without holding a family meeting, if there is a family. Mine was on the ninth day, and I was released after 12 days. Dr. Solomon and the social worker prepped me for the meeting. "Domenic, your job is to listen to your family in this meeting. They have concerns, and instead of spending meeting time defending yourself, I advise that you assure them that you hear them." The social worker advised me that Dee and my three daughters, Bianca, Dominique, and Gigi, would be in the meeting. Zach was away at college, but I did speak with him on the phone to tell him that I was alright.

At 10 a.m. on Monday morning, I entered the conference room. Dr. Solomon and the social worker were already there; they were my team. Bianca, Dominique, and Gigi came in shortly after – they had to be checked into the locked ward. We waited for Dee to arrive; she was a little late as usual. She was visibly upset. Dr. Solomon opened the meeting by introducing himself and the social worker, and the girls gave their names for the team's reference. "We're here to discuss Domenic's mental health, since it's our opinion that he will be discharged soon. But before we do that, we want to get input from the family." He asked Dee her concerns, and she wasn't shy to point out that before hospitalization and for months prior, I wasn't myself. She explained how I had written the two emails to her and her best friend (both emails were, admittedly, very nasty), and how I had verbal altercations with other people including my brother Fred's girlfriend (that argument was initiated because I felt that his girlfriend had too much influence in my parents' health care decisions, and she was fairly new to the family). Anyway, these incidents were out of character for me. Dr. Solomon then asked my daughters for their input, and they gave individual versions of the same story: that for the past few months, I wasn't the dad they knew for so many years. They described how mean I was to other people, other than themselves; and that, as Dominique described, I was very fidgety with things like the radio dial and heat controls in the car. It was painful for me to hear how much I had hurt them, and what they had to endure to set me on the path to resignation to my illness. Dominique wrote about her emotional struggle from the time admitting me to Newton-Wellesley

Hospital to the present in her personal statement for application to medical school:

Personal Statement:

"Dad, everyone's concerned about you. Will you meet Bianca and me at the MGH emergency room?" I called my father, who was in the midst of his second full-blown manic episode in five months, and begged him to meet my sister and me at Massachusetts General Hospital to undergo a psychological evaluation. The discomfort I felt on that February morning in 2019 brought me back to 2006; I am on the verge of tears as my mom helps Velcro me into a light pink, rigid plastic back brace that feels more like a medieval torture device than a tool to treat my scoliosis. While each of these events influenced my decision to become a doctor, all I could think about was the benefit that would come from facing the pain head-on.

My dad has bipolar disorder with psychotic features, and I knew from experience that he would not seek help alone. In his days of crisis, my dad turned into someone I did not recognize. Although this caused me intense emotional pain, I knew that I was capable of leading him to the treatment he so desperately needed. When logic and reason failed to convince him he needed help, I pleaded with him as only a daughter could. My dad went on to spend 12 days as an inpatient at McLean Hospital, but his recovery continued long after his discharge. In supporting him, I found myself feeling alone and unable to understand his behavior. I enrolled in the National Alliance on Mental Illness' Family to Family class, a 12-week course designed specifically for family members with loved ones facing severe mental illness. By learning the effects bipolar disorder has on my dad's brain, I was able to find him under the veil of his illness. I know that without the support of my sister and me, my dad would not have received the care he needed. As a doctor, the way I deliver care will be shaped by this experience. My patients, like my dad, will face barriers to care, and it will be my responsibility to employ different tactics to reduce those barriers. My approach will vary depending on the situation, but the end goal will always be the same: to treat the whole person.

After realizing my own transformation with my dad, I jumped at the opportunity to co-lead a NAMI class of my own. In the fall of 2019, I met my first group of students. Their stories and despair felt eerily similar to mine when I took the class. Through my students, I have learned that my real value as a teacher comes not from the facts I recite, but from the material that I humanize. When I share details about my experience caring for my dad as it relates to the curriculum, I see my students come to life. They relate to my anecdotes, then share their own hardships. Based on their situation, I highlight sections of the material that are relevant to each of them. Through this exchange, I see hope slowly replace the frustration and exhaustion etched in the faces of my students; and, over the course of 12 weeks, am proud to see the same transformation in them that I saw in myself. I know that if I want to succeed in transforming my patients' lives, as I have my students, I must connect with them on more than just a transactional level.

As a research technician in Dr. Rueda's lab at MGH, my time is split between enrolling patients in our gynecologic-focused tissue bank, coordinating sample collection, and using the samples to test novel anticancer therapeutics. Not only has this job given me a greater appreciation for the role of biomedical research in advancing clinical outcomes, but it has also given me insight into caring for the human being inside every patient. I will never forget consenting a woman on the 22nd floor overlooking the twinkling lights of Boston's skyline the night before her surgery. She was all alone and visibly anxious. What began as a standard conversation regarding the details of our research study, turned into a 45-minute conversation about coming to terms with a terminal illness and a candid discussion about death. At the end of our conversation, she voiced her satisfaction in knowing that if cancer was to take her from this world, at least she could be part of a study that was working to ensure a less grim prognosis for future generations of women. As I walked the deserted hallways back to the lab, I found myself feeling simultaneously overwhelmed and motivated. While I knew deep down, I could not cure her cancer, I felt an incredible sense of duty to help her fight. I realized that simply lending my ear and commiserating with her was enough to provide the emotional aspect of care that she sought at that moment.

The discomfort I felt that first night sleeping in my back brace eventually faded, but the memory stays with me as a reminder of my introduction to the process of medicine. I have come to realize that treating an illness may be straightforward – prescribe a back brace or an antipsychotic – but treating the patient requires more. My goal as a physician is to build on the roles I have already assumed – the humanitarian, the educator, the listener – in order to provide the empathetic, holistic care needed to rid my patients of their pain. It will not always be easy, and there will be times when I will have to fight for my patients just as I had to fight for my dad, but I am willing and prepared to do so.

Dominique Zarrella

At one point Dee made a comment that I disagreed with. Dr. Solomon saw that I was about to react strongly, and he looked directly at me and said "Domenic, we're here to listen, right?" I retracted. I took notes, and these are the concerns that I heard:

1. Med compliance, since I had gotten off my meds twice.

2. Overall, the trust had been broken. Something which I would have to rebuild slowly.

3. Aggression. To the point that Dee had to call the police and was so scared that she filed for a restraining order.

4. Money and stealing the mortgage (I think this is the one I reacted to because I disagreed with it so much).

5. Changing thoughts because of hypomania – a see-saw.

Dr. Solomon acknowledged their concerns but said I had made a lot of progress in the hospital, and that should be taken into consideration. The social worker asked if I'd be returning home upon discharge, to which Dee responded "No." Since I had to have a place to go, the social worker informed me that we needed to determine an alternative. Dr. Solomon closed the meeting by asking if anyone had any final comments, which no one did. I got up, walked over to my daughters, and gave them a big hug. Dee was with them, and I asked her, "Do you have a hug for me?" She nodded affirmatively, and I hugged her. They left the room, and I followed shortly after.

I went to my room mentally exhausted and lay on my bed thinking there was no remedy for my relationship with Dee. It seemed to me that her desire was to lock me up in that mental institution and throw away the key. A generation ago, that's exactly what might have happened.

Now I had to find a place to go upon discharge, and my team needed to know 48 hours before. They had talked about releasing me on Wednesday, but Dr. Solomon felt that I was still too hypomanic to leave, and he wanted to give more time for the meds to act. This gave me more time. I called my friend Huck, who I had stayed with for a few days in the fall when all this had started, but he was reluctant due to the fact that I was so manic and psychotic upon entering the hospital that I needed to be with someone who could identify whether I was going off track. I texted my friend Paul Grautski, who had offered a room in his house – "Dom, if I had known that you were practically homeless, you could have stayed at my house" – but because his wife and eight children had come down with the flu, he couldn't make the same offer now. Now where would I go? More uncertainty.

Dee came to the rescue to my housing predicament with a

proposal: a sober house in Leominster named New Beginnings. A sober house?? Me?? Ironic that I thought that she was the one who needed a sober house, not me. One thing that I had gotten control over a couple decades ago was my drinking. But one of the women in her little posse had admitted her husband there for a long-term stay to treat drug and alcohol addiction, so Dee must have thought, why not? I was immediately against the idea because:

1. I didn't need a sober house.

2. It would give the impression to anyone who knew me that not only had I had a nervous breakdown (which I did), but that I also fell off the wagon.

3. How safe would a sober house be?

But I was out of options, and if I wanted to be released on Friday, I needed to tell them where I'd be staying by Wednesday. So I accepted the idea reluctantly.

During all this time, Jeffrey and Casey were all ears to my concerns about New Beginnings. Jeffrey, who had met Dee and our girls, had been hoping for a reunion of Dee and I for the sake of our beautiful family. But upon hearing where she had arranged for me to go, he wasn't being so optimistic any more. Casey simply thought "that bitch" was up to no good. And, of course, I was able to share my feelings in the group sessions and with the individual counselors on the ward. This helped a lot. No one could offer an alternative, but they were sympathetic. I was happy to have caring souls who were concerned about my well-being.

Chapter 9

Aside from having a place to live, I needed a psychiatrist and a counselor appointment set up in advance. The social worker would do this with my input. I agreed not to return to Pat Senior when I found out that my old psychiatrist, Dr. Michael Isaiah Bennett, was still practicing and had an opening for me. I had left his practice eight years earlier to be treated at Mc-Lean and then Pat Senior. He could counsel and prescribe in a 30- or 60-minute session – two birds with one stone. This was a psychiatrist that I trusted immensely, because he had guided me through many episodes in the 10 years he treated me, from 2001 until 2011. I had the most successful years of my career under his treatment, and Dee loved him, as she got to meet him a handful of times in my treatment. The reason that I had loved Pat Senior's treatment strategy was because, right from the beginning, she just made sense. My first psychiatrist at Island Counseling was an Indian woman who proposed adding a second anti-depressant to my med cocktail, in addition to the lithium and Risperdal – four meds total. At that first meeting with her, I relented. But after about a month of feeling no relief, I called back to Island Counseling to take that doctor up on her proposal. She wouldn't see me! Because I had balked at her treatment plan with two antidepressants, she decided not to accept me into her practice. "Domenic, I do have a nurse practitioner who can see you in a week, Pat Senior," the secretary advised. I agreed to the appointment, and when I described my predicament to Pat, that I was taking lithium, Risperdal, and an anti-depressant; but was still very depressed, she responded "Well, that anti-depressant obviously isn't working, so let's take you off it!" A few months later my depression subsided. Or the anti-depressant was caus-ing me to feel tired and fatigued. After more than two years of anguish that almost resulted in ECT treatments, I was free of major depression, although a lesser depression and lots of anxiety remained. I love Pat Senior! But I would return to Michael Isaiah Bennett, not Pat Senior, for my future treatment.

On Thursday, Jeffrey came to me all upset. His doctor had prescribed a new anti-depressant, and Jeffrey felt it was causing him to become suicidal. He couldn't get the idea out of his head. Not to mention that his discharge was also impending, and he really didn't want to return home to his mother. He had lived in a semi-supervised housing complex for the mentally disabled and wanted to return there. He somehow had a lawyer who was working on the paperwork to get him into that housing complex, but he accused the lawyer of "not having his best interest" in mind. He also complained about his psychiatrist on the ward for having prescribed the anti-depressant that made him suicidal. It seemed that the only people he was getting along with were me and Casey. I tried to reassure him that everyone wasn't against him and that the more he accused them, the less they would want to help him.

Friday came, and I was admittedly nervous. Gigi would pick me up and bring me to New Beginnings in the afternoon. She was at college about 20 minutes away, and I certainly didn't want Dee to pick me up. I said goodbye to my fellow patients, but before I left, I had to meet with my team. Dr. Solomon asked how I felt about the discharge (he knew how I felt about New Beginnings), but I said I'd accepted the idea. The social worker signed off that everything was in place for me to be discharged, and that I could leave the ward on my own volition. But Dr. Solomon wasn't finished. He reminded me of the Serenity Prayer:

Chapter 9

God grant me the serenity to accept the things I cannot change; Courage to change the things I can; And wisdom to know the difference.

I responded that I knew the prayer very well, and that I even knew the long version, which continues:

Living one day at a time; Enjoying one moment at a time; Accepting hardships as the pathway to peace; Taking, as He did, this sinful world as it is, not as I would have it; Trusting that He will make all things right If I surrender to His Will; So that I may be reasonably happy in this life and supremely happy with Him Forever and ever in the next. Amen.

Dr. Solomon wasn't done, however. "Domenic, you've taken every opportunity to help yourself during your stay here, and you've done a great job. The team here recommends that you train to become a peer counselor because you could benefit many patients with the insight you have into your illness."

The social worker nodded in agreement. I was admittedly feeling sentimental because, not only was I not expecting him to say that, but it was a huge compliment and was very reassuring that I would be okay.

The head nurse gave me a brown paper shopping bag with all my belongings, and off I went!

CHAPTER 10

NEW BEGINNINGS AT THE SOBER HOUSE

I texted Gigi after leaving the locked ward, and she was waiting in the parking lot. She greeted me and off we headed to Leominster, about an hour away. Although I wasn't looking forward to the sober house, I was looking forward to getting out of McLean and starting a new chapter in my life. Gigi and I made small talk about college and her life in general – she's such a joyful person that just talking with her would cheer anyone up, but especially her father. She dropped me off in the driveway of New Beginnings, told me she loved me, and off I went into the cold and dreary afternoon.

But I was angry and scared about moving there. That was confirmed when I met with Andy, the owner and director of the facility. (Facility? More like a large old house with even older furniture.) We reviewed my admission forms and the reason that I was there. Of course, the admission forms were intended for someone with a drug or alcohol addiction, and I didn't want to allow Dee to officially label me with that, so I objected. But Andy assured me that the form was harmless and encouraged me to fill it out. I left the "type of addiction" and "follow-up resources" blank, but shortly after I signed and submitted it, I regretted leaving those subjects blank, because I was scared that Andy would fill them in according to his liking. That's how much I distrusted this whole process. Also, Dee had paid for the first week, $150, and I mistrusted her paying for my stay out of fear that if she was in control of my fate, I would be there a long time. Shortly after that, my brother Joe and Bianca successfully rearranged it so that Dee would pay me $300 a week, out of which I would pay the $150 a week for New Beginnings and $150 a week for expenses. Meals were included in the $150 fee. But I continued to pay the mortgage out of my disability pay while she lived there.

Shortly after finishing with Andy, the house manager, Anthony, toured me around the house, introducing me to the men we encountered along the way. He showed me my new room on the second floor. A double bunk on the left side, and my single bed on the right by the window. The light-colored wallpaper seemed to be older than the house (if that's possible), dark brown painted woodwork, and old sheer curtains on the window. Worn hardwood floors with a plain colored carpet in the middle. But there were rosary beads hanging on a nail on the wall, so I hoped that was a sign that the Blessed Mother was watching over me even in this place that I despised being in. The locker in my bedroom with a combination lock on it didn't help reassure me that I was secure. Later, one of the men confided in me that if-and-when one of the men in the house relapsed and was going on a drug binge, they might come into your room and steal anything that wasn't locked up or nailed down.

Anthony could sense that I mistrusted being there, and my anger with Dee, so he brought me to the kitchen for a little talk. We sat down at the kitchen table, Anthony across from me, and he said "Domenic, resentment will get you nowhere, try to go along with this until something breaks for you." There's that word again, resentment. My resentment for Dee had built up over the years, until I finally let it out as all-out hatred in those past few months. At least it relieved the pressure, like a pressure cooker exploding into the air. Around this time Monsignor Doran began to assure me that Dee "Loves you very much," which he would reiterate multiple times in the next few weeks through texts, so I started to soften. I trusted and respected the Monsignor. And I took Anthony's advice right away setting my sights on getting to know the other inhabitants of my new home. My roommate, Matt, was in his late 20s or early 30s, worked full-time for a local construction company, and got up every day at 4:30 a.m. to catch a ride on the company work truck to Boston, or wherever they were working on that particular day. He had successfully treated his addiction for long enough so that he was actually looking for an apartment for himself, his new girlfriend, and his two young daughters. He still had a few hurdles to cross before being able to enact his new plans, like approval from his parole officer, who had been investigating this whole arrangement for a few months. But Matt was so excited to be living with his daughters again that his face was beaming. And getting up at

Chapter 10

4:30 a.m. and working outside in the cold New England winter was no detriment to going forward.

I began to think that if everyone in this house was like Matt, being here wouldn't be so bad. It turned out to be true that the majority of these men were no less trustworthy than the long list of characters that I had met in my long career in high-tech sales. But they had the misfortune of being labelled with addiction, and some of those unsavory salesmen were known as upstanding members of the community. Again, this wasn't everyone that I met in sales. Not at all. Not to give a break to the addicted, because some of them cause a lot of heartache for the ones who love them; but most of the men in the house had owned up to their faults, accepted the consequences, and were trying to move on in a life that had been so hampered by their mistakes.

As I met more and more of the men (at meals, TV time, and just hanging out reading the paper or whatever), I became more comfortable. So I could start to let my personality out. But I kind of hid the fact of how religious I am for fear of being thought of as holier-than-thou among these tough guys. That all changed during one of the in-house AA Meetings on the Tuesday night after being admitted, as we went around the room of about 22 men, each announcing their progress in the week since the last meeting; how many meetings they attended that week, and what challenges lay ahead for the next week: "Hi, I'm so-and-so, and I'm an alcoholic (or addict, or both). I've been sober for XX months, and I'm thankful for that, and for so-and-so (family member, friend, pastor, or whoever) who has supported me for so long," etc. etc. etc. Some men had no one to support them, maybe because they had burned so many bridges. As we proceeded around the room, we came to Lenny. He was in his mid-to-late 30s, white, almost six feet tall, and kind of stalky. Dressed in jeans, sneakers, and a sweatshirt, he could fit in anywhere in this middle-class town. He had a strong Boston accent, having grown up in the New Bedford/Fall River area of Massachusetts until coming to New Beginnings in good ole' Leominster for treatment. His cousin, who lived in a nearby town, had found this place for him, and maybe thought she could keep a closer eye on him here. She was about the only family he had left on this planet. "My name is Lenny, and I'm an alcoholic and an addict. I've been sober for 33 months, and I've attended six meetings in the last week." (At least four were required by the house). "I found a job this past week, and my goal for the next week is to see a judge to release the restraining order that my deceased former girlfriend put on me, so that I can see my daughter again." He continued: "I make the best of my time around the house helping cook and doing some cleaning, and I say the rosary every day at 3 p.m. because I love the Blessed Mother!" Wow! What courage! During my turn before that, I had said nothing of my faith or religion. Lenny became my new best friend, and after that meeting, I became more open; going to daily mass celebrated by Father Bill, Father Diego, or Father Juan at St. Leo's and not being shy about it. My prejudices were wrong, however, and most of the men in the house had strong religious convictions, even if they weren't outright open about it. The sayings on plaques on the walls said it all: "Let go and Let God," "One day at a time," a three-dimensional picture of an eagle with the words "Under His Wings" on it, and others.

The other thing that taught me about the men's faith was the "Our Father" at the end of every Tuesday AA meeting. All holding hands, they said: "Our Father Who art in Heaven, hallowed be Thy name. Thy kingdom come, Thy will be done, on earth as it is in heaven. Give us this day our daily bread and forgive us our trespasses, as we forgive those who trespass against us, and lead us not into temptation but deliver us from evil. For Thine is the Kingdom, the Power, and the Glory, Amen!" The faith of this group of men rivalled all that I had seen in my local parish of St. Leo's or the Knights of the Poor Farm monthly Catholic Men's group I've attended for many years. Their gratitude for just being alive and sober was unbelievable. They were grateful for everything positive in their life in the face of so many trials. Trials like being abandoned by one of their parents at a young age, having an alcoholic or addicted parent, being abused physically, emotionally, or sexually, and losing everything due to addiction. No doubt that they had ultimate responsibility for their addiction, but it seems that most of these men had been jolted by the consequences of their actions and were trying to make the most out of the results.

Lenny was no different. His father was a long-time alcoholic, and his mother died when he was 12. The pastor in the neighborhood Catholic church had befriended him and gave him guidance during his teen years. That's why Lenny became Catholic in his predominantly Protestant family. And that's why he adored the Blessed Mother! I came to find all of this out because Lenny and I would talk whenever a free moment opened up. Again, like Lisa previously at the Newton Wellesley Hospital psych ward, I couldn't believe that this man was still standing after all that he had been through. He became a juvenile delinquent, getting into street fights in his tough New Bedford neighborhood; and he got into drinking and drugs shortly after his mother died – yes, at age 12! He showed me the resulting stab wounds on his wrist, and the spot on his forearm where a bullet had glanced. But that wasn't the worst of it. Lenny spent time in jail; and one of the other men in the house told me that not only was he raped in jail, but he was repeatedly raped by another inmate – he became that inmate's "bitch." Jack, one of the toughest guys in the house, would remind him of that often, calling Lenny "bitch." Lenny hated that more than anything. He really hated it because the last thing you want to be in prison is someone's bitch. Now, I know nothing about this kind of life, and I don't pretend to. Even watching this kind of stuff on TV or in movies didn't do justice to the kind of trauma Lenny suffered in jail. I just heard this second-hand. I probably would have died of horror if I had actually seen this, or God forbid, been the victim of it!

One day after supper, Lenny and Jack got into an argument. I'm not sure what it was about. Maybe Jack was harassing Lenny for not helping enough around the house or for leaving a mess in the kitchen. Something trivial. When Lenny fought back, Jack called him "bitch," and Lenny reacted strongly. "Don't call me that! You know I hate when you call me that!" Lenny was no longer a fighter, or else something nasty would have erupted. Seeing the excruciating pain on Lenny's face, I got up from the dinner table and, reaching out my hand to shake Jack's hand; said "Jack, I know that you're the local tough guy in the house, but please don't call Lenny that because you know how much it hurts him." Not knowing what to expect next, I remember not feeling scared of what may result from my actions – I said it, and that's that. Jack immediately melted! He didn't apologize to Lenny, but he did back down from his aggression. Jack never called Lenny bitch again. Jack and I became good friends. Maybe that similar incident that I had with Michael (the arch angel) at McLean taught me something. Or maybe Michael's legion of angels was protecting me, like he promised me in that cafeteria at McLean. Never-the-less, my second attempt at employing empathy in a conflict situation was a huge success.

About this time, I started substitute teaching in the Leominster Public School System. I had done this before during 2011-2013, when I was unemployed and on disability and took on the role of Mr. Mom. The kids were all in school. I loved "subbing." Partially because the kids were so funny, and because it keeps you young. But also, as a father, I'm great with kids. There are elementary schools, a middle school, and the CTEi (the trade high school). I had taught at the middle schools previously. I went downtown to the school department, got re-CORYed, and off I went. I would go to daily mass at 6:30 a.m. before reporting to the school. The vice principals texted me when they needed me. Rarely the morning of the sub day, usually a week or two in advance. Because I could only make a certain amount of monthly pay while on disability, I could only work about four days a week. The pay was horrendous, but it wasn't hard, and I enjoyed it. Much easier than being a semiconductor salesman and much less stressful. It was exactly what I needed while my brain recuperated from the trauma of a nervous breakdown. The doctors told me two things at McLean. First, new research showed that six-to-nine months of good rest and low stress would allow the neural networks in my brain to make new connections, replacing the severed connections from the breakdown. I never had the opportunity to do this because it was always back to work soon after a hospitalization. Secondly, I was advised to concentrate on myself, getting myself better, before tackling the marriage.

One cold March day, I was at one of the elementary schools subbing for a teacher in third grade. About midway through the day, it was getting warm and stuffy in the classroom. In the winter, I always wear a quarter-zip sweatshirt unless required to dress up more. On this particular day, I had a quarter-zip with a t-shirt underneath. Standing to the side of the classroom while the kids were changing subjects, I lifted the quarter-zip over my head to remove it, and my t-shirt went up also, uncovering my chubby belly. A little blonde girl with big brown eyes standing near me looked up at me in total innocence and total honesty, and exclaimed "Are you Santa Claus?" I was slightly embarrassed, but that little girl did get a good mark that day, and she did survive to make it to fourth grade. And she did get Christmas presents that year...

I was sitting at the teacher's desk one day when I was subbing at another elementary school. It was between periods, and in walked a young teacher with one of the students, an Amerasian boy. They walked up to my desk, and the teacher exclaimed "This is Felix. He's a fourth grader, and he's a big fan of Mr. Z!" (my nickname to the kids). "When he told me this," the teacher continued, "I immediately asked him if he wanted to come tell you, and he agreed to it, so here we are." I reached out my hand and shook this young man's hand, looking him straight in the eyes, and said "Thank you Felix, I enjoyed teaching you." Of course, I had lied, because I didn't remember this boy at all. The good ones you don't remember, only the ones that give you trouble!

On another occasion, I was subbing for in-school suspension

with six or seven 11 through 13-year-olds in a large conference room with a large round table and bookshelves with books for middle school aged students. I directed the kids to pick out a book and read, figuring they might as well get something out of the day instead of wasting it away. "Mr. Z, this is my old girlfriend Jessica," said one of the boys, turning to the girl sitting right next to him. "We broke up about three months ago." I thought nothing of his comment but acknowledged his remark and continued reading my book. When I looked up about five minutes later, it became evident that they had gotten back together – they were making out right there in the conference room!

Another middle school experience was caused by two boys arguing over where they would sit for the class. One boy was sitting at a desk, and the other was complaining loudly that it was his seat. I told the boy who was standing to go find another seat. But he wouldn't listen, and a big tussle broke out. After warning the boy sternly (as sternly as I get, which isn't much) to take another seat, he didn't budge. My threats to call the dean didn't persuade him at all, so I placed the call to the main office, and the dean showed up minutes later; a tall muscular bald fellow that I wouldn't want to mess with. "Mr. Z, who's giving you trouble?" I pointed to the boy, and he was escorted out of the room; no doubt to in-school suspension. Later in the day, the teacher in the classroom next door poked in to see how I was doing, so I explained the situation to her, naming the boy. I was surprised at her response. "We usually try our best to work with that boy instead of getting him into trouble. He's been in literally 10 foster homes in his young life."

Teaching gym to fourth graders one day in the elementary

school, a boy approached me crying. "Johnny is making fun of me." I responded that this little boy with tears in his eyes should just ignore Johnny, but about 10 minutes later the boy was back, crying again. "Johnny is still making fun of me." Getting frustrated with the whole situation, and because I knew that it wasn't a major problem; I said to the boy "Then go punch Johnny in the face!" The boy looked at me bewildered, turned around, and left. I never heard another complaint.

Youthful innocence was tested one day when I was teaching about 16 second graders English. Sitting in a large rocking chair reading to them a short picture book on the planets while they sat on the carpet in front of me, I came across the planet Uranus. Upon pronouncing the name, one of the girls in the front row started to giggle. Barely holding back laughter myself, they could see the look on my face, and the whole class burst into laughter, myself included! The next day in the supermarket, one of the mothers exclaimed "Jack got a huge kick out of the fact that Mr. Z said Uranus!"

I also worked as a substitute tutor for special education students in that same elementary school. Some were in a separate classroom with a couple of other grades, being taught life skills along with math and English courses tailored to their ability. The children would mix with the other students during "specials," like gym, art, and media in a strategy called "inclusion." Other special needs students, who could perform at a higher level, were included in the regular classrooms with a tutor attached to them all day; either one-on-one or one tutor for two or three students. In addition, there was a separate accelerated program for gifted children with higher-than-average intelligence. I loved this approach to education, because it left no one behind. Attending this type of school allowed students to appreciate each other and to mix with all types of people, including every nationality, creed, and religion imaginable. Puerto Rico, Guatemala, Uruguay, El Salvador, Kenya, South Africa, Japan, South Korea, Vietnam, and Ghana were just some of the home countries of the children I encountered, along with the white, black, and Hispanic middle-class and upper-middle-class students. All living in this little city of Leominster. Twenty-seven different countries and/or creeds were represented at the school's international night.

One such special needs student was Lilly. I don't know where she was from originally, but my guess is Central America. I think she was born in the U.S. with her twin sister, but her parents were immigrants. I was subbing for a tutor, Mr. Martinez, who was out with a back injury. So I was there for five or six school days, tutoring Lilly and two other children. Some of these children are actually brilliant and can easily do the work but need someone to keep their attention on the teacher and a little boost if they don't understand a certain aspect of the coursework. Lilly was the sweetest little third grader that you could imagine. Shoulder-length, dark, wavy hair, about average height, and slightly chubby, she could pass for a non-immigrant. Also, she went in spurts of being able to do the classwork easily and then losing attention and falling behind. Mostly this happened when she was tired. I think she was on some type of behavioral medication needed to keep her going but which made her tired. But the reason I remember her is because one day, sitting at her desk, she was crying. I approached her and bent down to her level, asking what was troubling her. "Some of the kids call me un-smart, and it hurts my feelings." I tried to reassure her that she was truly very smart, and that those kids shouldn't have said what they said. But I couldn't help but wonder why a kid would antagonize such a sweet little girl. I was heart-broken.

Of course, there were many joyful occasions also. Like the time I was a long-term sub at CTEi (Center for Technical Excellence, or the trade high school) for a plumbing teacher who was out for hip surgery. I was teamed up with the other permanent teacher, who is a licensed plumber, so the kids did learn a lot. Plus, I had completed many plumbing projects while repairing and remodeling our own houses. I taught freshmen and sophomores. One day, two students were arguing about who was the best pipe solderer in the sophomore class. Becoming wise to this whole process of teaching (and of watching too many cooking shows), I challenged them to a "solder off" – a soldering contest. I told the whole class of about 18 students that, if they wanted to contend for the title of "Best Solderer in the Sophomore Class," they could compete. I arranged for the other teacher to draw up the ground rules. "Solder three joints on different angles of copper pipe, and we'll cut them open and inspect the inside of the joint. Whoever has the best solder joints wins." Four students vied for the title. Zach, one of the boys who was in the argument, won.

Also around this time, I started seeing Dr. Bennett every other week for prescriptions and counseling sessions. First for an hour session, then for 30 minutes. Bianca and Dominique accompanied me, wanting to learn more about my condition and help the father who had supported them in all their undertakings throughout their young lives. No doubt they were anxious about my well-being. Being prospective medical students also piqued their interest in the field of psychology. We discussed the three reasons for my disgust with Dee, especially the drinking and partying. The girls assured me that since they knew their mother well, the reason for her undesirable behavior was that it's her outlet for stress, not to meet men. This comforted me, but I thought she could have picked a different vice, one that wouldn't cause such a wedge in our relationship. As the weeks progressed, they would attend every appointment with me, as they got to know how much I had actually struggled through their years growing up. Maybe they could forgive me for my recent actions, and all the pain I put them through.

Bianca and Dominique

We also further developed and reviewed the "safety plan" that I had started writing in Newton-Wellesley, McLean, and Marlborough hospitals. It's basically a chart showing the symptoms related to my physical (how does my body react), emotional (feelings), cognitive (thoughts and thought process), and behavioral (things you do or don't do) when I'm feeling Good, Mild Distress, Moderate Distress, and Serious Distress. See my actual chart:

Dad's Safety Plan

Warning Signs	Physical (how my body reacts)	Emotional (feelings)
Feeling Good (1-2)	• calm • low BP • appetite ok • strong • gym • social • unifier	• peaceful • accurate • pleasant • triumphant • relaxed • safe • optimist • hope
Mild Distress (3-5)	• BP 125/84 • journaling • try to talk it out	• anxiety • I don't just say 'no'
Moderate Distress (5-7)	• tired • heart rate normal body tense • not productive	• powerless • defective • wishy washy • struggle w/decision I don't agree with • frustration • confused • anger
In Serious Distress (8-10)	• BP = 164/99 • tight leg • kneck pain • jerky/radio • talk fast • hypo-smiling • hear rate normal	• hatred • threatened • don't care about other things • I'm Jesus

Cognitive (thoughts & thought process)	Behavioral (things you do or don't do)	What are you going to do abut it?
• clear/specific • poor concentration • poor memory • motivation • confident	• friendly • loving • lovable • funny/humor • social • exercise • sales • actually productive	• enjoy • help others: kids, family • work hard • be myself • try to communicate • exercise
• marriage • family • job • kids • overwhelming • resentment	• same as above	• deal with stubborness, non-listening people • talk to counselor • meditate • exercise
• racing thoughts-> multiple • ruminations -> one thing • ideas of reference -> TV, media • able • specific people • frustrated • hatred • anger	• more social • bothered • not confident • scared • threatened • checking into emergency	• more invega • call doctor • meditate • exercise
• bad concentration • bad memory • ideas of reference • grandiosity • racing thoughts • exaggerate • psychotic thought disorder (all above)	• F bombs • email/text • religious more • no peace • off meds • not listening • loud music	• tell someone • ER • tell psych doc

Chapter 10

Bianca would eventually head off to medical school in early July, leaving Dominique as the sole attendee to Dr. Bennett's appointments with me. As time went on, I described my illness in more detail in these meetings: the deep depressions that lasted months and years, and the debilitating anxiety that didn't prevent me from getting up in the morning and going to work or driving the kids to school, sports practices, and games. And, worst of all, the cognitive impairment that made it so hard to keep a job in the prior decade. Maybe it was a side effect of the medicine, or the effects of long-term use of powerful neural medications, or the nervous breakdowns themselves that had severed so many pathways in my brain. But either way, from 2009 (the Great Recession) to 2019, I couldn't hold a job for more than 2-and-one-half years (at Emerson Corporation). My other two stints were one year at Eastern States Components and the three months I spent at ACC. The only job that I could do successfully was substitute teaching. Since Dr. Bennett knew how hard I tried, and how successful I was in the years he treated me before (2001 to 2011), he confirmed that my recent failures were from my disease, not from a lack of effort. He and Pat Senior had written letters to this effect in my applications and re-applications to Social Security Disability. But either way, a whole new world opened up to Dominique about how I battled in secret to maintain a normal family life in the face of surmounting odds. She started to attend weekly NAMI (National Alliance on Mental Illness) Family to Family meetings, a support group for loved ones of the mentally ill. It was a 12-week course. Then she enrolled in a weekend long training course to teach the class. And finally, she began teaching the 12-week class with a partner to other family members of the mentally ill, as she explained in her personal statement for medical school.

Cognitive skills are used to comprehend, process, remember, and apply incoming information, according to the Oxford Dictionary. They are: sustained attention*, response inhibition, speed of information processing*, cognitive flexibility and control, multiple simultaneous attention*, working memory*, category formation, and pattern recognition (quoting C8 Sciences). The ones with asterisks (*) are those which still affect me. They can start to decrease in a normal person in their late 40s, which is when I noticed the biggest change (2009). But for me it's 10 times worse than for a normal person. Psychology Today says cognition refers to, quite simply, thinking.

I was fast asleep at New Beginnings late one night and heard a ruckus downstairs on the first floor. Jack was yelling "Wake up, get up!" The words were muffled a bit, but I heard him yell for Narcan, and I immediately knew that someone was overdosing. I never went down there, figuring I'd just be in the way of the ambulance, which showed up moments later. The next morning, the guys were talking about it. It was one of the younger men in the house who overdosed, but he survived and was in the hospital recovering.

One day Lenny approached me for a favor. He had a court date at the Fall River Courthouse in a few days to release the restraining order that prevented him from seeing his four- year-old daughter. "Domenic, I'll pay for your gas if you can take me. It's really important, and I have no other way to get there." I wasn't subbing that day, so I agreed to take him. Since he would be in his hometown, he wanted to see two people: a Protestant pastor that had some of his personal items and a female friend who worked at a smoke shop. We jumped into my white Explorer and drove into the snowy March morning toward Fall River, about 90 minutes away. We made small talk along the journey, and Lenny enumerated how many years it had been since he had seen this friend that we were going to see afterward. I had a touch of the flu that day, so I just stayed in the car when Lenny went into the courthouse. Back to the Explorer about two hours later, he woke me up, happy that the judge had set a court date in 10 days to settle the argument.

We drove to the pastor's house, and Lenny collected his stuff, introducing me to the gentleman, slightly older than me. Then we visited the smoke shop. Lenny found his friend and came out with a bag. "Domenic, can we just stay here a few minutes, so I can vape this new flavor that Karen just recommended?" I was a little pissed and scared that I didn't know whether this new flavor was legal or not. "Lenny, just smoke it outside on the walkway," I said to him. Which he did. I remember thinking "What will my kids think if I got arrested for just trying to help this poor soul?"

Since I was going to mass daily (St. Leo's was only a short walk away), Lenny asked me if he could join me. We went for three days, and Lenny didn't receive communion because he hadn't been to confession in a while – that was our next step. But he was very serious about the mass. On the third day, I introduced him to Father Diego, the associate pastor. "Father Diego, this is Lenny. He's a friend of mine, and he enjoys your homilies." Father greeted him warmly, and they shook hands. Walking towards my car, Lenny said to me, "You know my name isn't Lenny, it's Dan." I never knew, so I asked him why everyone called him Lenny. "Because Anthony just coined that name when I came here."

Lenny also impressed me one afternoon when I was returning from subbing. As I walked to the entrance, Lenny was on the porch by the door. "Domenic, a constable was here a little while ago to deliver some papers to you. I told him you weren't here. If he comes back, do you want me to tell him that you're not here?" Lenny was willing to lie for me, risking jail time, to protect me. Pretty loyal for someone I had just recently met. I told Lenny to just let him deliver the papers. They turned out to be divorce papers from Dee, dated about six days after I wrote her and her friend those nasty emails.

A few nights later as I was preparing for bed, I heard a loud knock on the bathroom door across the hall. "Lenny, open the door! Lenny!" In a split second, I wondered why Jack made such an incident out of it, and then someone kicked in the bathroom door. I stepped into the hall to see Jack, and one of the other men leapt into the bathroom. Lenny was on the floor totally naked and unconscious, totally still. Jack immediately jumped down and yelled for Lenny to wake up, commencing CPR on his lifeless body. Other men came on the scene as I just watched from my bedroom door. "Someone call an ambulance immediately!" Jack administered the Narcan, but it was useless. I could hear the ambulance on its way until two police officers rushed up the stairs to evaluate the situation. My guess is that the police must go into a house first because the inhabitants may be dangerous. Up came two EMTs with a stretcher as Jack continued to pump Lenny's chest. As the EMTs worked on Lenny, it started to become obvious that he wasn't responding – too late for the

Narcan to have done its job. While he lay on the stretcher, some kind of contraption was put on him that raised both of his arms and pumped his chest as they whisked him out of the house. One of the officers stayed behind to question us. Later we got the call that Lenny was dead.

This left a somber tone around the house. It had been a while since the last death from an overdose. But I began to understand why Jack was so hard-nosed. It seemed like he was the lead on preventing these things and responding when they did occur. I got to know Jack better and some things about his personal life. It seems that he was a hard-working tradesman with a family until his business went south, then he became involved in drinking and drugs. Similar to Anthony, who had a wife and a daughter and a very successful restaurant in the trendy section of Worcester until the open bar (since he was the owner, it was open bar for him) became a problem.

When I saw Father Diego at mass shortly after Lenny's death, I approached him to inquire about Lenny's fate. I was concerned, because Lenny lived a rough life and hadn't been to confession in quite a while, although he was intending to before he died. Father Diego assured me that since Lenny showed his desire for God by going to mass, God would have mercy on him. I was relieved.

During this whole time I was unable to see my 10-year-old mentee, Jadiel, whose name means "God is my Fortune." A mentee is what the local LUK Crisis Center calls a Little Brother, a mentoring program much like the Big Brother program.

Lacrosse season had started for Zach at Purchase College

in New York, about three hours away. I hadn't seen Zach much during this whole saga because he was away at school. Dee and I would drive to the home games together, sometimes bringing a daughter or two with us. But we were getting along well enough to commute together for the whole season, which ended in early May.

My brother Joe would call me from Florida almost every night to see how I was doing: He was obviously concerned about where I was living. He had kept in touch ever since this whole drama started in January during my father's funeral. Not sure what I would have done without Joe during this time. He and Bianca played ambassadors between Dee and I for any disagreements between us, and it was them that had set up my weekly $300 from Dee. After about a month of New Beginnings, Joe started questioning me about my next stop on my wild ride – where would I live for the near future? Surely, New Beginnings was just a steppingstone to somewhere else, right?

That opportunity came one day when I had nothing to do and didn't want to just hang around the house. Scott, the husband of Dee's other friend in the posse, was in the kitchen with me, and I got an idea. "Scott, let's go to Central Mass Powersports and look at the motorcycles!" It was mid-March and, around New England, people start dreaming of spring around this time. On top of that, Scott had a Harley that he loved. But he hadn't ridden it in a couple years because of his addiction and some physical problems. He had a doctor's appointment that morning, so we agreed to meet at the motorcycle shop at 1 p.m. On the way home from our rendezvous, on one of the main roads in town, I passed a large white gambrel with a sign on the front "Roommate Wanted."

CHAPTER 11

ON MY OWN

I called the number on the sign, and a guy named Tony answered the phone. He seemed friendly enough, and explained to me that he had an apartment in his two-family house that he rented rooms in. He and his wife, Maureen, lived in a small apartment in the basement of this large older house, leaving the rest of the house to the three roommates. In effect, it was like renting a whole house and not simply an apartment. I met with Tony at the house; he showed me around and explained that since he and Maureen had raised their family in this bigger apartment of the house, they left all the furnishings for the people who would occupy it, right down to the pots and pans. Tony showed me two of the bedrooms; one for $850 per month and another for $750. Seeing my look of discouragement, Tony offered "I do have this bedroom that I wasn't planning to rent. You can have it for $500." Wow! Once again, someone was watching out for me... The room that I would rent also had a full-sized bed, mattress, and box spring, so all I would need is sheets and bedding to move in. Electricity, heat, cable TV, and internet were all included in the rent. It was early-March, and I gave a deposit to move in March 15. But I still had another week at New Beginnings. Knowing my fate didn't involve staying at New Beginnings indefinitely allowed me to feel more comfortable there.

It was a warmer day in mid-March when I moved out of New Beginnings and into the apartment. It was a sunny day, and as a bonus, it wasn't snowing. The winter snow was starting to melt due to the warmer spring temperatures recently, maybe in the mid-40s. The sun is getting stronger. Typical for New England at this time of year. By this time I was driving my white 2013 Ford Explorer, and all the possessions that I had with me at the time easily fit into it. The men at New Beginnings wished me luck and invited me to visit anytime.

Lawyers were starting to discuss a divorce settlement, and my lawyer is Maureen Brennan, an Irish esquire who is a tough straight shooter. I had approached Janie Lanza Vowles to represent me in the divorce, but she had to decline because she had represented both Dee and I when we sold our dream home about three years before. So Janie recommended a colleague, Jane Vittoriosso (I like the name, it's "victory" in Italian). But she accepted a new job after our first meeting, so she had to decline also. She recommended Maureen, however, and she's been my lawyer ever since. Although tough, like I said, she listens to me well. An added benefit is that Maureen is from out of town, a couple towns away, so she could be more objective. It's just the way it worked out. Maureen allowed me to retain her for

$500 and make small monthly payments until the divorce was finalized. Then she would be paid out of the settlement. What a blessing, because I had no money.

More lacrosse games for Zach with Dee at Purchase College, and we were getting along well – bringing food and drinks to the tailgates after the game. Zach is very athletic, and the coach at Purchase had recruited him from a showcase that Zach and I attended on Long Island two years before. His dream of playing D-3 college ice hockey didn't materialize after one gap year at prep school playing junior hockey, so he accepted the offer to play lacrosse at Purchase. He's 5 feet, 10 inches, about 180 pounds, and is very quick with a rocket shot. In other words, I loved watching him play. Much like the girl's field hockey games at Vassar, Tufts, and Babson. After the three-hour drive home, I would go back to my apartment alone, with a good memory of the day. Luckily, I had great roommates: Chris, in his mid-20s, who loves to play street hockey (which is big around here); and Elijah, also in his mid-20s, who at first was working at a plastics factory job that he loved, then moved to a landscaping job that he loved even more. His hope was to start his own landscaping business in the near future. But both were excellent roommates, as were Tony and Maureen as landlords. Every month, I would take money from my Social Security Disability to pay the rent. Like I said before, it kept me off the streets! Having such young roommates keeps you young, as does substitute teaching.

On Monday, April 8, Bianca, Dominique, Gigi, and I attended a National Alliance on Mental Illness Advocacy Day at the Massachusetts State House. NAMI presented a briefing on the hottest mental health bills that were being voted on in Washington, then gave us those briefs to give to the senators and representatives from our area that same day in their offices at the State House. The four of us visited those offices and mostly spoke to their staff. It was a rainy day, slightly cold, and was the first day that I visited the Massachusetts State House. But this sparked an interest in mental health among my three girls.

Unfortunately for me, around late May, the hernia that I was diagnosed with five years ago was starting to bother me more than it had in the past, so I decided to have surgery, since I wasn't working in a serious job. I wouldn't be substituting after mid-June, when school gets out. So I scheduled the surgery for June 18. Funny story: when I met with the surgeon initially, he examined me and confirmed that I had a double hernia, one on the lower right side and one in the belly button. He asked if my guts ever popped out and if so, did I have to pop them back in? I responded: "Doctor, if that ever happened, I would have come in a long time ago." He laughed.

I had an appointment with Dr. Bennett in the afternoon of Monday, June 17, and, of course, Dominique attended. Since my surgery was the next day, I decided to make the trip after the appointment in Brookline to East Boston to visit that favorite shrine, Madonna Queen of the Universe. I was optimistic about the surgery, but you never know, so I decided to ask the Blessed Mother to intercede for me for a successful outcome. But I had forgotten that the shrine is closed on Mondays, the only day of the week that it's closed, so I was disappointed but decided not to give up. I entered the Don Orione home for retired priests and religious across the street, and looked inside for their chapel, to no avail. After wandering around for about 15 minutes, I returned to the entrance. There was a young woman attendant there, about late 30s or early 40s, long brown hair and tattoos on her arms; so I decided to ask her where there was a chapel, knowing that there had to be a small chapel on the premises, aside from the main chapel which was closed. She tried to explain that there was a little-known shrine of the Blessed Mother across the street, part of the bigger shrine. But I didn't understand where she was pointing me to, so she stepped outside to show me.

From our vantage point we could see the main statue, about 40- or 50-feet high made of copper worn green, the Blessed Mother with her right-hand index finger pointing up towards Heaven, and her left hand down and open, pointing to the globe below her feet. About 40 feet in front of her was a 15-foot crucifix, Jesus' arms open like you sometimes see on crucifixes, instead of having his hands nailed to the cross. This means both that He is crucified but also risen from the dead. Anyway, the shrine is located on a hill overlooking Logan airport a few miles away. Jets were flying overhead with their loud roar. What Sheila (as I found out that her name was) was trying to point out to me was a grotto with another smaller statue of the Blessed Mother, Our Lady of Lourdes; this one being only about 10-feet high and to the left of the main shrine but on the same side of the street. With the rectory in front of it, it was surrounded by temporary chain link construction fences. She said that statue had mystical powers that nobody really knew about, and it was rarely visited by outsiders – just what I was looking for! In my 20-plus years of coming here, I never noticed it, because it was set back surrounded by light woods, the rectory, and some houses. The grounds looked a little overgrown, probably neglected due to the construction around it.

Sheila advised that if I had special prayers, that was the place to present them. Since I had pictures of the kids in my car from cleaning out my parents' house, I decided to go one step further than praying for myself, so I grabbed the pictures of Bianca at her Vassar graduation, Dominique's Tufts graduation, and Zach's graduation from Saint Bernard's High School in Fitchburg. Also, one of Gigi at her high school graduation from Nashoba Regional High School in Bolton. Nonna and Papa displayed graduation pictures of all of their 12 grandchildren in their living room, atop their entertainment center. My intention was to place these pictures under the grotto, next to the statue, and ask her special protection, and for their dreams to come true (Bianca's medical school, etc.). But the gate was locked! The temporary fence had a gate with a chain and padlock. Heartbroken, I went to my car parked close by and just sat there, pictures in my hand. I prayed to the Blessed Mother: "Was this meant to be?" It seems like it was not so, but why did Sheila lead me here and tell me of its powers, just to disappoint me?" I thought that, due to my surgery the next day, I wouldn't be able to return for a while, and it looked like the grotto was closed indefinitely, not just on Mondays. So I asked Saint Anthony, my favorite saint (both of my grandmothers adored him) for guidance as to how to enter. Saint Anthony is a Franciscan, from Saint Frances' monastery, and I saw a small sparrow fly over my car and land in a tree in front of me, looking right at me (remember, I was still hypomanic and maybe a bit psychotic). Since Saint Francis is the patron of animals, I asked him if that bird was a sign that I was meant to enter into the grotto? Immediately the sparrow left his perch and flew over the fence into the grotto! I took that as a sign that I would be able to enter. I grabbed the pictures once again, got out of my car, and searched the perimeter of the fence for a point of entry, but found none. Maybe I could find a place to climb over it? Desperate, I went back to the locked gate. I pulled on the chain and lo-and-behold, the chain was long enough to open the gate for me to enter. The person who locked it didn't wrap the chain around the gates enough times to hold it securely closed.

Excitedly, I entered and approached the grotto, kneeling down on one knee and making the sign of the cross before entering another short, permanent wrought-iron fence with another gate. I approached the grotto and knelt again and started praying. "Blessed Mother, please bless my children – Bianca, Dominique, Zach, and Gigi. Protect them and intercede for them. For their health, aspirations, and faith." I then placed the pictures on both sides of her feet and left the grotto, making the temporary gate look locked as I had found it. Just after that, I saw Sheila across the street in her old black Chevy Tahoe getting ready to go home. She noticed me as I went over to tell her of the miracle that I was able to enter the Grotto by the birds' guidance. She wasn't surprised. I explained to her about the pictures I had placed there, and said that I must be crazy for doing this. Admitting that I have bipolar disorder, so I am a certified maniac, she motioned with her finger to her head, circling her ear with her index finger to imply that she was crazy, too. She said, "Tell me about it, I am too!" That's when I asked her name, and we parted ways.

I successfully had my surgery the next day and had a lot of discomfort but not a lot of pain. Gigi had picked me up the day of my surgery at 9 a.m. in our 2003 Saab convertible. Since it was a sunny day, we drove from Leominster to Worcester UMass Memorial Hospital with the top down; Gigi cruising on I190 South way above the speed limit of 65 m.p.h. This is the same highway that I had taken to Island Counseling for my appointments with Pat Senior. My thoughts were – will we get in an accident on our way to the surgery? The hospital called me on my cell phone, stating that they had a cancellation, and asked whether I could make it to the hospital early to take up some of the slack in their schedule. I responded that I could, being that I had left ample time in the schedule.

Gigi parked the Saab, and we entered the front door of the hospital, up to the day surgery waiting room where we checked in. Luckily for me, it wasn't a long wait, because my surgery was pulled in, and the staff was trying to prep me quickly for the newly scheduled start time. She stayed with me until Dr. Choi visited with me to review: "Hernia surgery for the right lower abdomen and an ambilocal hernia?" "Yes Doctor." After the anesthesiologist left, so did Gigi. She assured the nurse that she would be picking me up, following the protocol that I couldn't drive myself home. The staff wheeled me into the operating room, and the next thing I remember is being in the recovery room, waiting for a nurse to come check on me. It wasn't long before she entered, took my blood pressure and pulse, and reassured me that the surgery was successful and that I was doing very well. All my vital signs were normal. They had me blow into a little plastic contraption that measured my breathing. I had to show my ability to breathe deeply in order to avoid pneumonia. "As soon as you can, would you go to the men's room and assure me that you can pee?" These factors would determine my discharge time. But getting up from that hospital bed was no laughing matter, even with the nurse's assistance. I felt like I was going to pop, and my entrails would burst through my stitches, but the nurse assured me that they couldn't.

When I was cleared, at approximately 6 p.m., they informed me that Dee would be picking me up, but she was running late. Typical Dee. I waited as they started closing down the recovery room, until Dee came up, and she and the nurse escorted me in a wheelchair to Dee's car awaiting us at the front door. As we drove to my apartment, I could tell that she was very tense by the way she constantly tapped her thumbs on the steering wheel. I gave her direction to the apartment, and she dropped me off, commenting that it was nicer than she had imagined. Walking gingerly into the front door, I resolved to make the best of my recuperation. Every time I had to rise from the couch to pee or to fix lunch or dinner, I had to do a crunch. Not painful, but certainly a concern since the first few days would be crucial to my recovery.

It would take six weeks before I would begin to feel normal again, but in the meantime I stayed fairly active. Since I couldn't work or do much else, it gave me the time to write this book. Sometimes on the Lancaster town beach on Spec Pond, sometimes in the Leominster Public Library. But the Saturday after my surgery, Headly came to town to visit his family. Since I missed his February visit due to my stay at McLean, I set up another meeting of the gang, and so I went. Four days after my surgery! Headly, Moody, Huck, and Bells were there. We just had drinks and a lot of laughs at my favorite restaurant and pub, the Rye and Thyme in Leominster. Laughing is not your friend four days after hernia surgery, let me assure you.

On the next Saturday morning, I was at the house at Cleverly Cove picking up some things when I went into my workshop in the basement to get a tool to give Zach, and I saw a wedding picture of Dee and me on one of the shelves. I picked it up and put it in the Milan, where I had an individual picture of Dee and an old picture of our young family at Easter time, when Gigi was less than one year old. Again, these other pictures came from my parents' house. The next day, Sunday, I had an idea; take the three pictures of Dee, our wedding, and our family to the Madonna Queen of the Universe shrine. I would pray for Dee, our marriage, and our family, so threatened by the times we live in. So I made the one-hour journey, hernia and all. It was Sunday afternoon. I also brought with me rosary beads that were my father's years ago, given to me by my mother, again during a cleaning out of their house. The specialness of these rosary beads was that they were given to my father by the parish priest at the time, Father John Capuano of St. Anthony's. I had noticed a long time ago that, coincidentally, Father John was a benefactor of the Shrine because his name was engraved as such on one of the plaques there.

I attended 4:30 p.m. mass at the Shrine. After the mass I approached the priest, evidently from Central or South America by his accent, and asked him to bless my own personal rosary beads, which he did. Was it a coincidence that it was mine and Dee's 29th wedding anniversary? I gathered these beads, together with my father's, and headed to the grotto, intending to place the three pictures there. When I got to the gate, the padlocked chain was much tighter this time, and I couldn't enter. Discouraged again because I thought I couldn't put Dee's picture, and the others, into the grotto, I approached the rectory and asked the priest how I could enter. He had no idea. Again, I searched the perimeter of the fence but only saw a door to the basement of the shrine that opened up into the grotto area. It was closed, but I had the idea to go into the shrine and find that door. I went into the shrine on the third floor and descended the stairs on that end of the building. Another stairway to go down into the basement was dark, and each level had a fire door from the stairway to the floor connected to it. When I entered the stairway, I placed a block on the bottom of the door to keep it open, in case it would lock behind me, trapping me in the stairway upon my return.

I found that basement door and opened it. Sure enough, it led to the grotto area. I left it open so I could return through that route, walked to the grotto with my pictures and rosary beads, and knelt before entering it, as I did the previous time. I placed the pictures of Dee, our wedding, and the one of our young family to the sides of Mary's feet. The pictures from my previous visit were still there. I said my prayer for Mary's intercession. "Lord, I pray for Dee. And especially for our love, marriage, and family to be restored." Noticing that the Blessed Mother's hands, outstretched together as in prayer, were not graced with rosary beads as they sometimes are in statues of her, I dangled my father's old beads over her hands. They were hanging down about 12 inches from her hands, with the crucifix at the bottom. I had brought them back to the priest who gave them to my father 50 years ago, Father John. Now that I was successful in my endeavor, it was time to depart. I was only there a brief time for fear of being discovered. I returned to the open basement door and climbed the three flights to the level I had entered at, but the stairway door I had blocked open was now closed – and locked! Panicking, I descended back down the stairway, checking each level for an unlocked door, to no avail. I opened that basement door again. Leaving it open once again, I entered the grotto area and anxiously searched for a way out. Since I left my cell phone in the car because I was entering a sacred place, I had no way of calling anyone if I couldn't get out. Again, I searched the perimeter, this time from the inside, and found an area of the fence that I could scale down into a back yard that led behind the grotto and out into the street. I was free! I remembered that the basement door was left open and decided to leave it that way instead of entering again by my new pathway to the grotto. After all, I had just had hernia surgery. The Milan waited for me and my quick getaway. But I successfully completed my mission in this sacred mystical place, anticipating that my prayers might someday be answered.

I returned to the shrine a few weeks later, after another Dr. Bennett appointment, hoping to receive some kind of sign that my prayers were accepted. As I approached the grotto area, I noticed that the gate was slightly opened. When I got to the gate, the chain and padlock were again on the gate, but loose enough for me to fit by, like before. Once again, I was able to enter the area. When I got to the statue of the Blessed Mother, after kneeling again before entering the wrought iron fenced area, I said a prayer. I looked for the pictures that I had left at her feet, but they weren't there. However my father's rosary beads that I left there were still dangling over her hands. As with all of our prayers, we surrender them to God's will, not our will.

CHAPTER 12

BIANCA'S RIDE LET'S DO SOME-THING ABOUT IT

Domenic and Bianca

Domenic with Bianca at Spec Pond, Lancaster, Masssachusetts June, 2019 before her ride from Boston to D.C. for mental health awareness. For further details on Bianca's biking adventure, go to her blog at RaisingAwareness1.weebly.com

B ianca always had empathy for me. It seems that from an early age, she knew I was suffering, although most people didn't notice that I was carrying this cross almost alone. To raise awareness for mental health and the people suffering from it, she rode her bicycle solo almost 500 miles from Boston to Washington D.C. to meet with senators and representatives to lobby for mental health bills that were up for vote – the ones we had gathered at the NAMI Advocacy Day in April. She sent me the following postcard from Washington, D.C.:

**Bianca's postcard
from Washington, D.C.**

Chapter 12

**Back of Bianca's
postcard to Domenic**

Dear Dad,

I am sending this postcard to you from D.C.! Thank you for your help with my gear and bike, and for believing that I could do it. I know it surely made a statement to the senators/reps and many people along the way, but I hope most importantly it makes a statement to you. I don't want you to feel like you need to battle this anymore. I know your story can inspire other people and bring awareness.

I love you! Bianca

She wrote the following in her early acceptance essay to Vassar College in 2011:

A.P. Literature, Mr. Smith

My Role Model

People come and go throughout our lives for certain reasons unbeknownst to us as individuals. No matter how long these people stay in our lives, their influence on our existence is what they are remembered for. Similar to many people, my greatest role model is one of my parents. However, unlike most other stereotypical parents, my father suffers from bipolar disorder and manic depression. Despite these obstacles – and perhaps because of them – he is an incredible person who has influenced me in many ways. Not only has he been a positive role model who inspires me and also allows me to be thankful for what I am blessed with, he has shaped my life's purpose.

Regardless of my father's struggles, he is still a very good man. It inspires me to see him encouraging our family to go to church every Sunday and to see his endeavors to rise above his condition. As challenging as it is, he does not give up or become discouraged. He has never once let anything come in the way of the love and responsibility he has toward his family. This encourages me, because it shows me how hard he works to overcome his struggles for the betterment of my siblings and myself; he puts others first. I always strive to succeed in whatever I do realizing that I do not have those challenges. I want to make the best of every moment of my life and not give in to petty things like peer pressure or laziness. If my dad did not let the disability of depression get to him, I am never letting someone pressure me into wasting my life.

In addition to my father's inspiring actions, there are some things that he does without being aware of it. His mental illness brings everything into perspective. When things become tough, I remind myself of the worst. I am extremely thankful that he has chosen not to resort to alcohol or drugs to help himself cope. This shows me his strong personality and that anything is possi-

ble. I was given a full life to live with no boundaries, like my dad has, and I want to make the most of it.

Seeing my dad suffer is not something every daughter has to deal with. A lot of the time, I sympathize with my father. Why did he have to have this damper put on his life? However, one relenting question always finds its way back into my mind: Why is his mental disorder so different from a broken bone? I know the mind is more difficult to understand than a physical problem, but there has to be a similar solution. I have always known that I wanted to be a doctor of some kind, so I have been looking into the medical field. Since I have experience with depression through my dad and have the personal drive to solve its complications, I feel as though I can make a difference.

My father's mental illness has had a significant impact on my life. There are the obvious disadvantages of the sickness, but I have also been optimistically influenced by him. His strength in character has provided a strong and steady role model for me, as well as allowing me to keep everything in life in perspective. Ultimately, when I fulfill my dreams of graduating medical school, where I will search for the answers to this misunderstood disease, my dad's influence could be the result of a cure for Depression.

And my response is below:

Lessons in Love

How to be Loving to Everyone!! (…and I Mean Everyone!!)

November 21, 2018

(THE DAY BEFORE THANKSGIVING)

Receiving the Gifts that God wants to give you.

To achieve the Life that God wants you to have.

Bianca,

Unbeknownst to us, sometimes God places in our Lives someone who drives us "Absolutely Nuts!!"

Why He does this, and what He expects us to do with this situation or person, is sometimes beyond our capacity. But everyone faces this in life, especially those who wish to do exceptional things.

Ultimately, Trust in God is the desired effect that He's trying to bring about and surrendering these situations or people to Him. But practically speaking, the answer is to "Hate the sin but Love the sinner." Love them because God is trying to bring you to a new level, and this situation or person is the instrument that He's using to bring about this growth. That's why He doesn't just take it away, no matter how much we pray that He does. Hate the sin, because loving someone doesn't mean accepting their

Chapter 12

abuse, not if you want to be at peace inside yourself. It doesn't mean giving them everything they want, which would be spoiling them. But since, ultimately, we only have control over ourselves (and sometimes, for some situations, we don't even have that!!), we shouldn't try to control the other person. Neither should we totally avoid them if God is constantly placing them in our path (God is the "Crazy" One).

Sure, some people come into our lives, create complete havoc, and then leave permanently. I can easily let go and forgive these people, although it might take time. But what about the person who we work with, or a relative, or someone we truly like, but one aspect of their personality simply rubs us the wrong way. Yes, if we have a choice, we could simply move on and use our energy for more creative things. But what about the people in our lives who don't or can't move on? What about the teenage child who is "into drugs" (which is ultimately a cry for help), or the husband who has bipolar disorder (which is ultimately a chemical imbalance that needs balancing)?

Practically speaking, we need to find the inner peace to articulate to this person that what they're doing, or not doing, is hurting us! Sometimes we have to be tough. What if they don't respond, or if their response is to attack us or to say that our attitude is the problem? Usually, if this is a long-standing problem, then we've tried to resolve it before, but we've gotten this type of response. We may never resolve it.

The answer is to forgive the person, even if they haven't asked for it; although we may not reconcile with them and become best buddies with them until they've regained our trust. Indeed, we may never reconcile with them. But in the meantime, our inner disposition for them needs to be one of Love and not of Hate. Hate and resentment (the slow release version of hatred) only tear us up inside. It's a fine balance, and sometimes we will lose our way, because rarely do we handle these situations 100 percent correctly – that's life on earth. We sometimes will hate— but we shouldn't beat ourselves up because we did. Also, setting boundaries with difficult or pushy people, or limiting our time with them or having an exit strategy (remove yourself from the situation temporarily) may be a solution. Finally, getting advice and support from people you trust is priceless. Fight or flight is banished.

But, for me personally, always being "nice" to people who drive me nuts is not only hypocritical, but people can see right through it. My challenge is to move from passive/aggressive (another word for bipolar) to confidence (another word for believing in myself) and to assertiveness (another word for fearlessness), so I can realize the unique plan that God has for me. Confidence and fearlessness are traits that I learned from your mom (now I know why God placed her in my life, even when she was the person "driving me crazy"). Traits that you kids have. But I also need to retain my beautiful traits—loving, empathetic, and a unifier. Also, traits that you kids have!! You're doubly blessed!!

In your letter "My Role Model," you show amazing insight into the disease of mental illness. Insight that mentally healthy people simply don't possess. Your medical school "Personal Statement" shows similar insight into the interior struggle of people with mental illness. This insight (the gift of empathy), which you learned from observing my struggles, will give you an amazing advantage as a cardiologist or other type of medical doctor; while the gift of confidence, which your mom exudes, will allow you to be tough on patients who want to invite you into their pity party of self-absorption. Wisdom and experience will help you know which gift to apply and when. These gifts will also help you in your personal life.

In your "My Role Model" letter that I cherish, you hope that "my dad's influence could be the result of a cure for depression." That letter carried me through many dark days, until your dream and my prayer could finally be realized in a healing of depression – my depression. A healing, because "depression is anger turned inward" and "resentment is like swallowing poison and expecting your enemy to die." Love for our enemies is a healthier response but very tricky to understand in practice. The genetic dimension of my depression is still there in my brain, but why throw gas on the fire by throwing in a dose of hatred? Or self-pity? Or blame? By learning to love instead, maybe I can start looking forward to the successes (both personally and financially) that life may bring my way from what I learned from this disease. I'm optimistic.

You're a very loving and courageous young lady. You're committed to your dreams but flexible enough to face the curve balls that life will inevitably bring. You take time to have fun and be adventurous. You care deeply about the people you love. In other words, you got all the gifts of your mom and I combined, like all of our kids did. I can't wait to see where they will take you. But more importantly, I'm proud of you for what you've already accomplished in your short life. Your first cure, God willing, a healing of depression – my depression!

Why does God allow bad things to happen? So He can bring a greater good out of them!

Love,

Dad

And she wrote, for her medical school essay to the University of New England, where she now attends:

Bianca Zarrella   August 2018

Application Essay for Medical School

Milestones; an action or event marking a significant change or stage of development.

For me, I consider becoming a physician a journey and like any journey, there are milestones.

I have faint recollections of my first milestone. I remember the worried looks of my parents, their kindness, and bravery when they first discovered that I was born with a congenital heart defect. That was the bad news. The good news was the fact that a new, less invasive procedure to implant a closure device in my defective heart valve had been developed. And so begins my journey of becoming exposed to the world of medicine. Over the next 15 years, I went for monthly and then yearly follow-up evaluations and developed an ever-growing admiration for the doctors and health care professionals with whom I came in contact with. Their dedication, knowledge of science, compassion, and ability to change the outcome of a serious problem in a positive manner was truly inspiring. I began to see how a career in medicine truly makes a difference for the good in this world.

Chapter 12

I learned about the undeserved stigma associated with some illnesses that further complicate and burden the patients seeking wellness by watching my kind and loving father struggle with mental illness. There was no surgical implant to cure his bipolar disorder, only trial and error treatment in medications and talk therapy with multiple psychologists. Unlike my supportive and straight-forward experience, he was forced to battle his illness is silence. The situation has to end, not only for him but also for the good of society.

I believe I developed considerable leadership skills, which will make me a more effective physician, through sports. At first, numerous technical rules and unfamiliar skills seemed as daunting as finding a cure for mental illness. With guidance from coaches, I developed the insight to break long-term ambitions down into short-term goals; the mastery of each new technique and ability to run a sub-six-minute mile led to my MVP award. As captain, I worked with the coach to identify players' skills, set benchmarks for our players, and develop new winning game strategies. Sports taught me many lessons applicable to real life and a confidence I will carry with me forever.

After my junior year at Vassar, I was able to research under Dr. Jason Kim at the University of Massachusetts Medical School. I joined a new team where lab members advised each other, presented journal clubs, and collaborated on experiments. I learned firsthand how data is gathered, and conclusions were made, and how signaling pathways affect and determine cellular function. Under Dr. Kim's direct guidance, I learned the world-renown hyperinsulinemia-euglycemic clamp to assess insulin sensitivity in vivo. When he noted that my steady hand would make me an excellent physician, I knew my dreams of becoming a doctor were in reach. This experience made me realize that diabetes is a constellation of comorbidities, so it is important to look at all perspectives when approaching a difficult problem.

I currently have the privilege of working at MGH in a dual role focused on gynecological malignancies. As clinical research coordinator, I interact with patients and families daily seeing the current surgical and chemotherapy management options. I am one step ahead as a research assistant, assessing treatments to target stem cell markers. The past six months, I taught an OB/GYN fellow the techniques to guide her through her thesis research. She struggled to complete the project, and equated her experience to being "dropped in a jungle without a map." In comparing my conversations with the post-docs, it seems scientists strive to fill knowledge gaps and are rewarded for asking the right questions, whereas clinicians are rewarded for knowing answers. Wondering if such divergence hinders translation of scientific discoveries into medical advances leaves me with an aspiration to connect the dots across medical silos.

I want to encourage different specialties to combine forces and care for one patient holistically. Like defense and offense work together on a sports team, scientific advancements and clinical practice should be symbiotic. Modern medicine calls for a team of not only clinicians and scientists, but pharmacists and mental health counselors, as well as statisticians and engineers. After all, supercomputers helped sequence the human genome.

As a physician, I would have a strong commitment to the

interdisciplinary team approach to the diagnosis and management of disease. I feel that going forward, this approach is the best model for delivering high-quality affordable health care to all. We have a fiduciary responsibility to deliver nothing less

Bianca Zarrella

My comments in her introduction to the representatives and congress, for her bike trip, were:

To greatly increase the success rate of mental health treatment in this country, alternatives to the emergency room for acute instances, exit strategies after acute hospitalization like the NAMI Compass Program, and multiple levels of in-patient hospitalization depending on the degree of illness, like McLean has, could be employed. Sharing the in-patient records with the outpatient treatment team should be made easier, without all the red tape required today.

I don't agree with fail-first med strategies where lower-cost alternatives are tried first—time is the asset. In a perfect world, drug companies could develop advanced meds at lower cost. The second-generation Invega antipsychotic that I was prescribed at McLean cost $1,200 a month.

Social Security Disability with Part A (Hospitalization) Health Insurance are steps in the right direction. But mandatory coverage and full parity for mental illnesses, short-term housing, and a better understanding of the relationship between addiction and mental illness, would create a saner society.

I'm incredibly proud of Bianca, who is using her many gifts to give back to those less fortunate than her. She'll make an in-

credible doctor!

Dominique, after attending the NAMI Advocacy day in April, and many of my appointments with Dr. Bennett, decided to get involved with NAMI. First, she took a NAMI course for family members and friends of the mentally ill. It met weekly for 12 weeks. Then she trained for a full weekend on how to teach the course. Then she taught the 12-week course with another instructor, as she explained in her personal statement. She left the luncheon after my mother's funeral to give a speech at the NAMI statewide convention. Her talk was about being a family member of someone with serious mental illness.

I'm also incredibly proud of Dominique. She'll also make an incredible doctor!

Gigi and her classmates at Babson developed a website – thedormroomproject.weebly.com — for mental health awareness for college students. In her class on marketing and information technology, she and four others from her team created this website. It has 150 members signed up, and it helps students identify the signs of mental illness in themselves or their friends, so that no one suffers needlessly through ignorance of the symptoms. It also shows you how to support those that you love or go to school with, and there's a discussion group on the website.

Gigi will make an incredible corporate lawyer, if she decides to pursue that path.

Zach's participation in supporting mental health is much more subtle. He supports me by encouraging me to enjoy the peace of the outdoors: fishing, kayaking, hunting, which are meditative in themselves. Shooting at the range, riding motorcycles, boating, working on his truck, his helping me with house projects to relieve the burden of owning and maintaining a house, and attending his ice hockey and college lacrosse games helps me to enjoy life to the fullest. We spend a lot of time together.

Zach will make an incredible environmentalist.

Shortly after completing her bike ride to Washington, D.C., Bianca headed off to medical school.

Dee and Bianca with Representative Ayanna Pressley in D.C.

CHAPTER 13

THE LONG SUMMER OF 2019 AND INTO THE FALL

By now it was late June, and my medicines were doing their job, and I was getting much needed rest in my new home, my apartment. Moody and I would get together most weekends for a couple beers after I was well enough from my hernia surgery. I would also visit Huck and Dawn periodically. Their friendships were greatly needed at this time, and I would also have dinner often with Moody and his parents, Janet and Arnold, at their house — sometimes swimming in their backyard pool before a hearty barbecue. I spent the 4th of July with them.

Chapter 13

I spent lots of time writing this book, most times on the Lancaster Public Beach after buying a seasonal pass for $60 and buying a beach chair and a couple beach towels at the local Target store. I also visited Nonna for hours at a time. While writing this book outside on the patio of her rehab facility in Ayer, Massachusetts, or at Saint Elizabeth's Hospital in Brighton, I would check on her in her room often. Her heart was failing, and she needed aorta valve replacement surgery, which was eventually performed in August. But in the meantime, from June and through the summer, she was in and out of the hospital and rehab facilities. She continually encouraged me to keep writing while I visited her, sometimes with her on the patio outside the rehab facility. I can still envision her sitting in her wheelchair enjoying the sun shining on her face.

One beautiful, hot and sunny summer day, when I was sitting on the beach writing, I texted Dominique for something, and she texted back that she was on the boat. "Do you want to come on the boat?" That was an offer that I couldn't pass up! I drove over to the Fire Road, parked the Milan, and headed down the stairs to the boat dock. The water was clear and warm. Dominique saw me from the middle of the lake and then drove the boat to the dock where I jumped in. We spent a couple hours cruising and chilling in the middle of the lake, alternating between jumping into the lake off the swim platform and catching some rays on the boat. I hadn't been on the boat since earlier in the season when Dee and I were getting along, but I had recently stopped visiting because Maureen Brennan and I were discussing the details of the divorce. Hence no more boat rides for Domenic until this sunny day with Dominique. So it was a treasure. As we listened to Bob Marley on the boat's stereo, we talked about how her life was going, my mental health, and how it was for me living at the apartment. All of the kids were concerned about my living arrangements. Was it safe? Were the accommodations acceptable? Were my roommates trustworthy?

Walking on Water

Zach invited Huck and I to go fishing one Thursday afternoon at the Wachusett Reservoir, about a 15-minutes' drive away in central Massachusetts. We drove in Zach's truck to a secluded spot on the reservoir, which was a 20-minute hike from where we left the truck. This reminded me of old times, when Zach was in his mid-teens, and we would ride in Huck's 2003 GMC Sierra 4x4 pickup to transfer Zach's minibike to various trails. The weather was perfect on this particular day, and we fished for two or three hours in the best of conditions. Each of us caught a couple fish until we left the beach at sunset. Catch and release. After fishing, we rendezvoused at my apartment to split a six-pack of Voodoo Ranger IPAs as we compared fishing stories. It was the first time Zach and Huck saw my apartment, and they were relieved to see how nice it was. A large granite and stainless-steel kitchen open to a tall high-top table with barstools where we sat, and also open to a large dining room and carpeted living room. Other than the living room it was all hardwood floors. I showed them my bedroom upstairs – very simple with the full-size bed, the white comforter that my godfather's mother, Rose Nutilie, had crocheted for my and Dee's wedding, and stacks of my cloths, mostly shorts, bathing suits, and t-Shirts. Chris and Elijah's bedrooms were also upstairs.

Domenic at Wachusett Reservoir

Gigi and I would have dinner occasionally at one of our favorite restaurants: Il Camino for great Italian food or Asian Imperial for sushi. She was working out on strength training and cardio for her upcoming Babson field hockey tryouts. Normally, I would go to the gym with her, but recovering from the hernia didn't allow that. I could eat, however, with no adverse effects on my stomach!! On one occasion, I barbecued thick fillets on the grill with baked potatoes and corn on the cob. Gigi was surprised that I could cook so well.

Bianca was away at medical school, and Gigi and I visited her, taking her to the beach in Biddeford, Maine, one hot day in late July. She couldn't even take a break from studying, as we reviewed parts of the upper arm for a Monday morning anatomy quiz. We stopped for some delicious Maine lobsters and ice cream before parting ways and heading back home the same day.

Bianca, Domenic and Gigi

Moody and I made daytrips to Newport, Rhode Island, a few times that summer. Second Beach for the day and the Landing Restaurant and Beach Bar in the evening. Second Beach is one of my favorites in New England. Long sandy shores with warm water, a concession stand along with outdoor showers, and bathrooms that you could wash up in and change your clothes after leaving the beach, before heading to the Landing. On one particular night, with a live band playing and people dancing to the music, we were just going about our business when we started talking to three women who were in Newport for the weekend. It was our custom to reach out to other patrons to make small talk, and we made many friends at that bar. With all the sun, music, and dancing, I could see why Dee loved to visit Naples, Florida, with her friends. Great places for singles or couples. Not exactly where married people belong with their friends on a regular basis, unless you're separated like I was. Anyway, these women were in their mid to late 40s and were out for some fun. One of them, Maria, was recently divorced, but I'm not sure about the other two. Moody had a lot of fun dancing with her, but I kind of held back on the dancing because of my precarious relationship with Dee; we weren't divorced yet. The live music was so loud that I could barely hear the girls talk, but we made conversation anyway – I found out that they were all sisters. Maria, Diane, and Lori. Lori was the youngest, and her sisters liked to tease her about her faith because she was quite outspoken about it. After much conversation about Newport, comparing the beaches – 1st Beach, 2nd Beach, and 3rd Beach (how imaginative), we talked about the music there, and what kind of music we liked, etc., but not much about our personal lives. I never found out if Diane and Lori were married, nor did I care. I just wanted to have some conversation and some fun.

"Domenic, I'm a Baptist, and I love Jesus," Lori blurted out. "I'm a Catholic, and I love Jesus, too," I responded. Now sometimes Catholics and Protestants shouldn't talk deeply about their faith, but I took a chance. "I think we have more in common about our faith than we have that's uncommon, since we both love Jesus," I said. She affirmed it. "God is good even when things are bad," she repeated many times in our conversation. I could confirm that God is good, even though things weren't ideal for me, given my marital situation with Dee. I don't know who brought up the subject, but I related to Lori that I thought heaven was open to Catholics, Protestants, Jews, Muslims, Buddhists, and for that matter, all people. "After all, God is God, and He can do anything He wants," I argued. But beyond that I don't understand. And there's no doubt in my mind that it will be Jesus who judges us, although many people reject Him. She responded that there were certain things about the Catholic faith that she liked, like confession, and I shared that there are many Protestant ministers that I enjoy listening to, like Dr. David Jeremiah, Dr. Charles Stanley, and others on WDER 92.1 in Northern Central Massachusetts and Southern New Hampshire. Sensing my openness, she shared that "Catholics are cooler than I thought." Then she proclaimed something I wasn't expecting in our casual conversation. "You're going to change the world!!" After thinking about it briefly, I determined that the only way I could change the world is through this book, and the sharing of my faith through the experiences of my life. We all parted ways to talk to more potential friends, and Moody and I left for home at 11 p.m., given that we had a 90-minute drive ahead of us.

We made other trips to Newport and made more friends, but none as notable as Lori. Moody and I share a love for the beach, since he lived in Southern California for 30 years before moving back home, and he worked on Martha's Vineyard renting mopeds in the summers during college. I visited him there often, listening to Bob Marley, UB40, and the English Beat. Two of my grandparents are from Gaeta, Italy, which is "the San Diego of Italy" with its expansive beaches and warm, dry climate. We went to Cape Cod (the Cape), Hampton Beach (New Hampshire), Maine, and Rhode Island beaches often as kids.

Chapter 13

Fall is field hockey season, bringing the excitement of the competition and the comradery of the fans. This year was no different, with Gigi playing her sophomore year at Babson College in Wellesley, Massachusetts. McDowell Field is the venue for home games, during which Jack Diamond traditionally hosted pre-game in the "Forest," a small clump of trees behind the field, and a post-game tailgate that included hot dogs and hamburgers cooked on the grill, plus a variety of home-cooked delicacies served on picnic tables. Sometimes we would be treated with raw oysters as an appetizer. Time in the Forest was spent getting the parents and fans warmed up for a lot of yelling and cheering during the match, mostly at the refs for questionable calls. Half-way through the season, the Forest was closed down by school officials for the rowdiness, but Jack would usually find a local establishment to get us ready for the game. It was a thrill to watch Gigi score an assist against Keene State during her rare play time.

On Saturday, September 14, 2019, Bianca had her White Coat Ceremony at medical school, the University of New England. I picked Gigi up at Babson after a field hockey practice, and we drove to Portland, Maine, where the ceremony was held. We met Bianca and Dee at the ceremony. About 200 students got their white coats, and I was so proud of her for pursuing her dream of becoming a doctor. Afterward, Dee, Bianca, Gigi, and I went to dinner at a local noodle shop.

Gigi, Domenic and Bianca

Zach and I pulled "Walking on Water" out of the lake in late September. Before winterizing it, we hauled it up to Lake Monomonac on the Mass/New Hampshire border for some boating fun. Lake Monomonac is about 500 acres and has great boating and many cottages along the shoreline. Moody came along with us as we used Zach's truck to tow the boat. Piloting it to drop it in the water or pull it out can be nerve-racking to me, but since Zach was operating the truck, it was up to me. I had just gotten my U.S. Coast Guard boating license a couple weeks before and knew all the rules of the water – i.e. what the different colored buoys meant, what to do when passing other boats, water safety, towing tubers and skiers, etc. We found out how fast the boat can go as we opened up the 225HP inboard/outboard like we could never do on Spec Pond, because it's less than 70 acres. Forty-five m.p.h. was the top speed. It was a sunny and warm day for late September in New England, about 75 or 80 degrees and a little windy. A beautiful day for Zach, Moody, and a couple of Zach's friends who joined us. One of them, Tyler, lived on the lake.

CHAPTER 14

LOSING NONNA

On October 18, 2019, we lost a beautiful soul. My mother, Nonna, as we call her, passed away in my arms at the Keystone Nursing Home and Rehab facility in Leominster. I subbed that day at Francis Drake Elementary School, and got out of school at 3:30 p.m., heading right over to Keystone to visit Nonna. She had just been transferred from the rehab side of the facility to the nursing home side, turning her Medicare over to nursing home care – this would be a permanent move. It troubled me that although her aorta valve replacement surgery at St. Elizabeth's was successful, her body was failing, especially her kidneys. But I had hoped that she would recover well enough to live in an assisted living facility, not a nursing home, because she was still very lucid – sharp as a tack. She would frequently ask me "Why am I still here? Why did God leave me here; I want to be with Papa!" I would attempt to explain that maybe God left her here for her grandchildren or even for her great-grandchildren – I was thinking that Nonna would be an ideal candidate to pass on the Faith, like she did to me. As we talked that afternoon, she joyfully spoke about the visit she had earlier that day with her cousins, Anita and Ray. They all grew up in Somerville, Massachusetts, and were very close. Their visit brought back many childhood memories, allowing her to forget her destiny in the nursing home briefly while they reminisced with her.

Nonna and I talked about her visit with her cousins, and she was always interested in hearing about my kids. "How does Bianca like medical school?" "How does Dominique like her new apartment in Somerville? How is her job at Mass General? Is she applying to medical schools?" She would rifle through each child: "Zach and Emily (his girlfriend at the time) visited me yesterday and brought some cupcakes and a decorated pumpkin. He said he likes Fitchburg State University" (where he had transferred to). And finally, she would ask how Gigi was doing in field hockey at Babson, and how her studies were progressing. Nonna loved everyone, and she especially loved Dee. But during the whole separation, she supported me fully, never saying a bad word about Dee, but disappointed at how she had treated me.

The staff brought Nonna her dinner, and she would always offer me a portion. "I'm not going to eat this soup," or it was the chicken, or a fruit. Food is important to Italians, especially Italian grandmothers. As she finished her meal, me sitting right beside her at the table, we continued talking. As we discussed my day at the school, she reached over and grabbed my arm with her hand and said "Dom!!…. Dom!!" Then she collapsed as if fainting, and I jumped out of my chair to support her as she fell to the floor. "Nurse, nurse!!!!! Please help!!!!!" An aide came running in. The aid took her pulse as Nonna laid lifeless on the floor of that nursing home room. The aide looked at me with a frown on her face. As the aide called for more assistance, Nonna took a deep breath, as if it were to be her last, and she passed away quickly. Since she had a DNR (Do Not Resuscitate), the nurse that entered could only wait until they declared her deceased a few moments later. I felt so sad.

I notified Fred that Nonna had passed away peacefully, and he came to the nursing home with Barbara, his girlfriend. They had been caring for Nonna and Papa the last few months. We made calls to our siblings who made plans to fly out as soon as possible. I remember the deep loneliness that I felt while waiting for the undertaker to come pick Nonna up at the nursing home. Angela came with my nephew and god child, Matt, and his new wife, Savannah, before Nonna was taken away, and we all got to say our last goodbyes. After Nonna was taken, we started to pack her things, loading them into Fred's car to be taken back to their house. I had plans that night to have a few beers with Moody, Bells, and Mario, but I called Bells to cancel after notifying him of the bad news. He must have been thinking: my friend lost his father, his mother, spent time in a mental hospital, and is going through a divorce – all within nine months. I went back to my apartment alone, but I was more relieved than crushed. Nonna passed peacefully and wouldn't have to live in a nursing home, but I would miss our visits and her valuable advice. She was a loving and encouraging mother, and I spent a lot of time with her, not just during this summer but all my life. Dee and I never took the opportunity to transfer my job far away because of family, although it cost us dearly financially in those lean years. We valued family and prized knowing that my parents were always there, especially during my first nervous breakdown and subsequent years battling the disease. As I did with Papa, I had no regrets having spent the last few months of their lives very close to them.

Dee was one of the first people that I called, right after my siblings, and she expressed her condolences.

Planning Nonna's funeral was the next step, as Joe and Rob arrived to help with the arrangements. The routine was fresh in our minds, since Papa's funeral was so recent. Fred, Barbara, Angela, and myself met with the funeral director, and Angela, Rob, and I met with Father Juan from St. Anthony's Church to choose readings and hymns.

I saw Dee a few days before the funeral, and she asked what the arrangements would be for the funeral. I gave her the viewing hours at the funeral home, and the time of the funeral. I invited her to go through the procession line at the wake with the kids, and to sit with them at the funeral. I would sit with one of my brothers or my sister. I could tell that she didn't like my plan. "So, I'll be with the kids?" "Unless you want to stand with me in the line at the wake and have our family sit together at the funeral," I responded. She liked that idea. Now that I made some kind of peace with her, I decided that maybe I could make restitution for my meanness to her best friend at Papa's funeral, where I specifically told her not to come! So I texted Dee later: "Please invite your friend to Nonna's funeral services. I can't be mad forever!" Her friend took me up on that offer, and she and her husband attended the wake.

Chapter 14

It just so happened that Bells, Mario, Headly (who was coincidently in town from Boise), Moody and his parents, and Huck arrived at the funeral home for the wake at approximately the same time, so they teamed up and came through the line together. I showed them a picture that I had found just recently in my parent's house of Headly with Mario's father, who was playing the guitar, at mine and Dee's wedding after party in June 1990. Headly was hamming it up as usual with his arms spread behind Mario's father. I gave the picture to Mario. The atmosphere lightened immediately when the gang went through the line, and even Dee got a laugh. Before that, it was kind of tense between Dee and me. Chris came through later, and his family restaurant, the Il Camino (Nonna's favorite) sent flowers.

As with all wakes and funerals, it was an opportunity to see aunts, uncles, and cousins – some that I hadn't seen because they live far away, and some locals who I hadn't seen because life is so busy. My double cousins (my father's brother married my mother's sister), John from Maine (I have three first cousins named John after my grandfather, so they all have a nicknames), and Tony from San Diego (Patty's brothers who gave us the Milan), were present. I had called both of them the day after Nonna passed away, and Tony said he would try to make the trip to New England. Somehow, I knew that he would attend, even though he came for Papa's funeral recently also. Dee and I parted ways after the wake, and I went to the Doubletree Hotel bar and pub where John from Maine, his wife Wendy, Tony, and my brother Joe and his wife, Sandy, were staying. Tony's girlfriend, Nicole, had stayed behind in San Diego. We had a beer and some chicken wings, fried zucchini, and mozzarella sticks. Wendy asked how Dee and I were doing, and I skimmed over it, only explaining the part about the finances but not about her escapades. I guess that I just didn't want to get that deep into it at the time, although I'm close enough to these cousins that I could have.

Once again, the funeral was beautiful! Once again, it was at St. Anthony's Church in Fitchburg, and Father Juan officiated. Father Bill, from our parish, St. Leo's, co-celebrated. Bianca, Zach, Rob's daughter Tiffany, my nephews Danny, Matt, Corey, and Josh were pall bearers. Dominique read the first reading, and Gigi did the second reading. Father Juan proclaimed the gospel, as is customary at any mass. Danny, Angela's son, gave the eulogy which her other son, Matt, helped him write. And once again, this small Catholic church was packed.

The first reading was:

Philippians 4: 4-8 King James Version

Rejoice in the Lord always, and again I say, Rejoice. Let your moderation be known to all men. The Lord is at hand.

Have no anxiety at all; but in everything by prayer and supplication with thanksgiving let your requests be made known unto God.

And the peace of God, which passeth all understanding, shall keep your hearts and minds through Jesus Christ.

Finally, brethren, whatsoever things are true, whatsoever things are honest, whatsoever things are just, whatsoever things are pure, whatsoever things are lovely, whatsoever things are of good report; if there be any virtue, and if there be any praise, think of these things.

The responsorial psalm was:

Psalm 23 {A Psalm of David.}

The Lord is my shepherd; I shall not want.

He maketh me to lie down in green pastures: He leadeth me beside the still waters.

He restoreth my soul: He leadeth me in the paths of righteousness for His name's sake.

Yeah, though I walk in the valley of the shadow of death, I will fear no evil: for Thou art with me; Thy rod and thy staff they comfort me.

Thou preparest a table before me in the presence of mine enemies: thou annointest my head with oil; my cup runneth over.

Surely goodness and mercy shall follow me all the days of my life: and I will dwell in the house of the Lord forever.

The second reading was:

Isaiah 40: 1 – 11 King James Version

Comfort ye, comfort ye my people, saith your God.

Speak ye comfortably to Jerusalem, and cry unto her, that her warfare is accomplished, that her iniquity is pardoned: for she hath received double for all her sins.

The voice of him that crieth in the wilderness, prepare ye the way of the Lord, make straight in the desert a highway for our God.

Every valley shall be exalted, and every mountain and hill shall be made low: and crooked shall be made straight, and the rough places plain:

And the glory of the Lord shall be revealed, and all flesh shall see it together: for the mouth of the Lord hath spoken it.

The voice said, Cry. And he said, What shall I cry? All flesh is grass, and all the goodliness thereof is as the flower of the field:

The grass withereth, the flower faideth: but the word of our God shall stand forever.

O Zion, that bringest good tidings, get thee up into the high mountain; O Jerusalem, that bringest good tidings, lift up thy voice with strength; lift it up, be not afraid; say unto the cities of Judah, Behold your God!

Behold, the Lord God will come with strong hand, and His arm shall rule for Him: behold, His reward is with Him, and His work before Him.

He shall feed His flock like a shepherd: He shall gather the lambs with His arm, and carry them in His bosom, and shall gently lead those that are with young.

(Coincidentally, further on in Isaiah 40 is verse 31, the last verse, is one of my favorites):

But they that wait upon the Lord shall renew their strength; they shall mount up with wings as eagles; they shall run, and not be weary; and they shall walk, and not faint.

Chapter 14

This was the Gospel:

John 6: 37-40

All that the Father giveth me shall come to me; and him that cometh to Me I will no wise cast out.

For I came down from heaven, not to do mine own will, but the will of Him that sent me.

And this is the Father's will which hath sent me, that of all which He hath given me I should lose nothing, but should raise it up again at the last day.

And this is the will of Him that sent me, that everyone that seeth the Son, and believeth on Him, may have everlasting life; and I will raise him up at the last day.

Father Juan's homily centered on Nonna being welcomed into heaven, because she was a faith-filled woman who leaned on the Lord. Although a Columbian, not an Italian, he reiterated that "Faith, Family, and Food" were most treasured in Florence's life.

The attendees were invited to my favorite restaurant, the Rye 'n Thyme, for a luncheon after the burial. Joe spoke after the formalities of the burial, valuing Nonna's contribution to raising him and the rest of his siblings, and being the proud grandmother of 12. I joked with Mario, Huck, Moody, and Joe at the Rye 'n Thyme bar during the luncheon. Joe and I had owned a boat after he and I graduated from college – a 19-foot, 140HP Renken Bow Rider. Both Joe and I had girlfriends all the way through college, so we didn't hang around much together, although we're only 15 months apart. But back then we were girlfriendless, and we both shared a love for boats, and therefore teamed up to buy this one in the summer of 1984. But Joe and I were the odd couple, me a partier at the time, and Joe a strait-laced, more conscientious young man. We each told our version of the stories when Joe, Huck, Mario, and I drove my 1975 Chevy Blazer 4x4 from Leominster to Manahawkin, New Jersey, to pick up that boat. I cleaned the Blazer from top to bottom for the trip, and about 20 minutes into that roadtrip, Mario yelled: "Dom, did you clean the truck?" as he crushed a Bud Light can in his hand and flung it at me while I was driving! We got to Manahawkin six hours later as the final touches were being done to the Renken, planning to hitch up the boat immediately to tow it home. But there were delays causing us to stay overnight. Since we weren't planning on staying over, we had dinner at a local seafood restaurant where Joe ordered "Halibut for the Hell-of-it." Mario, Huck, and Joe all remembered that incidental of the story, but I added another classic Joe remark that none of them recalled: the young waitress had a string of six earrings going up her left ear – not as common then as it is today – and Joe asked her "Did you fall on a fork or something?" That night we slept in the boatyard: Joe and I in the Blazer, Huck under a dinghy, and Mario found a 32-foot Sport-fisher in drydock that was unlocked, so he slept in there. We laughed and laughed.

My mother's only remaining sibling, Aunt Betty, and her husband, my Uncle Leo, were also at the luncheon, as was my Godmother, my mother's cousin, Rose English. Rose is also very devout, and I have an interesting story about her. She lived about an hour from me, in Canton, Massachusetts, so our interactions were mostly by phone. After Dee and I were first married, we tried to start a family right away. But there were challenges – we had two miscarriages. Relating this sad predicament to Rose one evening back then (1991), she proposed a solution: "Domenic, I'll mail you a St. Gerard prayer card. He is the saint of motherhood." I received the card, and Dee and I both began to pray it. Shortly after, Dee's gynecologist had an idea. Instead of waiting for a third miscarriage to investigate the source of the problem, she would prescribe progesterone, a female hormone that can cause miscarriage in women. If a woman was deficient in progesterone, the same outcome that we witnessed would be repeated. So, on a hunch, she proposed that Dee start taking the drug immediately. Wellaah, Bianca was born!!! I held on to that card for over 20 years, but at my cousin Patty's funeral a few years ago, I returned it to Rose, thinking that it might be useful to someone else now. The last Christmas card that I mailed to Rose had a picture of our four kids in Christmas attire, on which I wrote "Thank you St. Gerard!" on the back.

After the luncheon, we all took a break from the social side of things and went back to our homes or hotels, then the cousins returned to the Rye 'n Thyme for a Zarrella cousins' night. More beers and socializing, and a lot of Cokes for me after I had reached my three beer limit for the day. Tony, John, my cousin John Francis and his sisters Anne and Angela, Laura and her sister Paula from Sanibel Island, Florida, and my sister Angela and brothers Joe and Rob, were there. The conversation centered on the fun family times of childhood.

I have mixed emotions regarding the deaths of my mother and father. I miss them dearly but am relieved that they died peacefully at an advanced age. I enjoyed much time with them before they passed, as I did throughout their lives, and they were blessed with not having to spend endless years in a nursing home. Additionally, Nonna got her wish – to be in Heaven with Papa.

CHAPTER 15

LIFE GOES ON

Halloween was held in Leominster on Saturday, November 2, as was my 40th High School Reunion. The pre-reunion get-together was at On the Rocks bar on the waterfront of Lake Whalom in Leominster. The reunion was at the Monoosnock Country Club. About 100 of my 500 classmates attended, but I spent most of the night with Bells and Mario – I'm not sure why, because I usually try to avoid these two characters! Huck, Moody, and Headly were also there.

Thanksgiving came quickly and once again it would be a holiday away from family life. I baked a turkey with stuffing and all the fixings and invited my sister, Angela, and her son Matthew and his new bride, Savannah, plus Angela's older son Danny and his boyfriend Doug, to my apartment for dinner. I cleaned that apartment from top to bottom, knowing that Angela's family was coming over, but I also invited my kids over for dessert. They showed up with chocolate chip cookies, chocolate cream pie, and apple pie. Zach and Emily joined Bianca, Dominique, and Gigi for this after party. My girls and I played Monopoly into the night.

I was surprised to be invited to Zach's 22nd birthday party dinner on December 11 at a chic Asian restaurant in Southie, because Dee was going, and she had to approve me being there. Zach and Emily, Gigi, Dominique, Dee, and I attended. Bianca was away at medical school. We all drove together from Lancaster, except for Dominique, who rode her bike there – yes, December 11 in Boston! Unfortunately, there was only street parking at this restaurant, and not much of that. Upon our arrival, Dee spotted a parking spot, but it was very close to the corner of the street. Typical, Dee insisted that it would be okay, so we parked there. A nice $55 ticket awaited us when we returned to the car! But the more memorable event was that Zach and I shared his first glass of sake, of which we ordered a small bottle and shared it with the rest of the party. I had tried sake in Tokyo a few times when travelling there on business, but Zach and the others weren't very fond of it. I had given Zach a combination birthday and Christmas present a few days before. His present was the mounted buck head that we had brought to the taxidermist the year before, after he shot that first deer.

A white Christmas was merry because of the snow, but also because I would spend it with my kids again. I prepared for the traditional Italian seven fish dinner that we would share at my apartment on Christmas Eve. The apartment is large enough, and the kitchen well equipped enough, for a dinner party like this. I bought all of the seven fishes – calamari, shrimp, cod, mussels, scallops, smelts, and lobster – at various stores. The cod was served in baccala, or cod balls, but I added all the other types of fish into a red sauce that I started cooking the day before. The girls visited earlier in the day to fry the baccala, but with not as much success as Nonna had all those years. As we prepared the dinner, cooking baked macaroni to enjoy with the red sauce, I asked the girls what Dee was doing for Christmas Eve. Gigi mentioned that she was probably wrapping presents for the big day, Christmas, the next day. So I texted Dee, inviting her for the Christmas Eve dinner, but she declined, remarking that she had a lot of wrapping to do. At the end of the night, however, the girls invited me to the house the next morning, Christmas morning, to open presents with the family. Again, I was surprised, because I knew that Dee had to consent to me being there. Zach and Emily joined us for Christmas Eve dessert, and we laughed as we enjoyed an éclair ring and anisette cookies that the girls had made earlier in the day. The night ended as the kids presented to me the first gift of Christmas, the traditional Christmas pajamas that I would wear that night. At about 9:30 a.m. on Christmas I headed to the house to open presents, and it was very amicable. The girls gave me a dumbbell weight set that I had requested, a black Babson quarter-zip sweatshirt, and a precious group of four inch by six inch pictures taken over recent years. Zach was excited to give a new fishing pole that could separate into two pieces to fit in the Milan, since I started fishing with him more in the fall. I gave the girls gift cards, and since I had already given Zach his combined birthday and Christmas present December 11 at his birthday dinner, I only had a small gift for him.

Money was tight but manageable at Christmas, but my Social Security Disability and part-time work subbing was enough to buy the Christmas presents. Having a manageable rent, which included everything like heat, electricity, cable, and internet, etc., helped. Tony and his wife, Maureen, were great landlords, living in the downstairs apartment. I had explained the precarious situation between me and Dee, and they understood. Maureen would always say "Things have a way of working out." I learned a few more lessons subbing. One: if a boy asks to go to the bathroom during class, you have to determine if he really has to go, or if he just wants to goof off. If he's holding his crotch, he's not joking! Second: If a student asks to visit the nurse, you don't really know if they're actually sick, or if they're just a hypochondriac. I tell them to wait 20 minutes and let me know if their headache, stomach ache, or bruise is still bothering them. If they return 20 minutes later with the same ailment, they're really sick. But most don't return! Third: when a high school student asks for a pass to go to the restroom, if they're wearing their backpack, they don't plan to come back.

New Year's Eve was a quiet one spent with Moody and his parents at their house. Next was the Super Bowl, which was the one-year anniversary of my meltdown at Mass General. But it was a good year, mental-health-wise, and the hypomania that lasted into the fall season had greatly abated. No more mystical experiences like those that I had at the Marian shrine in the summer. Moody's cousin, Lee, invited us to take a road trip to Apponaug Brewing Company in Woonsocket, Rhode Island, for the Super Bowl. Since road trips to Newport were out of season, a new activity of patronizing New England breweries with Lee had replaced it. We'd jump into Lee's four-door Jeep and head to any location in New England where there are breweries, which is everywhere these days.

Chapter 15

I have a friend, Steve Anastos, that Bianca stayed with on her 500-mile trek from Boston to D.C. She needed a place to stay in Stamford, Connecticut, to fill in the gaps between other nights along the way spent at the homes of members of her cycling club. Coincidentally, Steve's daughter Erin, who's about Bianca's age, suffers from anxiety. So the common bond of Erin's and my experiences helped cement their relationship. She planned to stay one night at the Anastos residence but added another night due to the friendship that she and Erin immediately developed. Another reason for the extra night was because Erin wanted Bianca to attend a DBSA (Depression and Bipolar Support Alliance) group session moderated by Erin's psychologist, Dr. John Tamarin. Bianca was so impressed with Dr. T that she insisted that now I attend one of his sessions, so we both made the trip to Stamford in mid-February, arriving Thursday night in order to participate in the Friday group in Greenwich. Dr. T has a large house with a huge office that easily accommodated the 25 or so people who attended the session. Some came as support for a loved one, as Bianca did for me, and Steve did for Erin. Erin told the story of Bianca's solo bike trip the previous June to raise awareness for mental illness, and Dr. T commented that she must love me very much! He has a very objective approach to the patients; empathetic but also not afraid to call someone out on their self-pity. Bianca and I stayed over Friday night and went to the Women's March in New York City on Saturday, to promote equal opportunity for women. Then we stayed Saturday night also, heading back to Leominster Sunday afternoon.

During this time I continued to attend daily mass, monthly "Five First Saturdays" confessions, and daily rosaries. The "First Saturday" of the month is dedicated to the Blessed Mother at Fatima, where Sister Lucia was asked to commence the practice – receive the Eucharist (at mass), confession, the rosary, and 15 minutes of quiet meditation on the mysteries of the rosary, with the intention of reparation for the offenses against her Immaculate Heart. All done on the first Saturday of every month for five consecutive months. If you do this, Mary will assist you at the hour of death. You can dedicate each five-month series to a particular person that you love. The Blessed Mother requested that the faithful do the Five First Saturdays and that the Pope Consecrate Russia to the Immaculate Heart of Mary, for world peace (don't we need that right now). The Consecration of Russia was done by St. Pope John Paul II on March 25, 1984, but the Five First Saturdays haven't been done in enough numbers, so world peace eludes us. The Blessed Mother also requested that the faithful pray the rosary daily. Do you believe that we can have world peace? I do!

I periodically texted Monsignor Doran, Father Anthony, and Father Augustine from the Abbey, providing updates on my relationship with Dee.

The divorce negotiations were ongoing during this time, and Dee and I traded terms back-and-forth through our lawyers. Assets like the house, the land, and cars were being decided upon, as well as the debts, of which there were plenty. I was entitled to alimony due to the disparity in incomes between us, but we were trying to work through all of this. I was reluctant to demand alimony because I knew it would bankrupt Dee; but, on the other hand, my living on Social Security Disability and substitute teaching would be tight. No way to live after having worked so hard for so long. In the end, our agreement included a lump sum for me but no alimony.

To make matters even more confusing was that although Dee was pushing hard for the divorce, she would invite me to events like Zach's birthday dinner and Christmas morning. One day I got a group text from her to me and the kids, inviting us to her niece's wedding on March 7, 2020. Maybe she wanted the divorce but also wanted to remain friends. I'm not sure, but I appreciated that our relationship was amicable.

Madison and Dan's wedding was beautiful and fun. Maddy is my god child. Emily sent me a text the day before, asking if I wanted to drive to the wedding with her and Zach, which I accepted. We took the Milan. It was a bright, sunny day, in the mid-40s, but windy. The ceremony was held at an inn in Amherst, Massachusetts where Maddy and Dan have a store, Mass Vintage, selling vintage sports clothing. Zach, Emily, and I had some time to kill before the wedding, so we visited the store. We spent time before the ceremony with Dee's nephew, Casey. Bianca, Dominique, and Gigi also attended, and they looked stunning in their formal dresses. I sat next to Dee at the ceremony and reception. Bianca, Dominique, Gigi, and I danced the night away. Zach and Emily also had a great time with a lot of dancing.

By this time the coronavirus was just getting serious in the United States. China and Italy already had their turns and thousands were still dying in Italy. Nobody really knew what was happening in China, because nobody trusted their reports. The lockdown started in mid-March, and I never really knew how much substitute teaching kept me busy until school was closed, and all the students would be taught remotely. But I wasn't alone. Except for essential personnel, people were either work-ing from home or not working at all. I kept busy by fishing, walking, and working out with the dumbbells the kids had given me for Christmas. A lot of watching the Outdoor Channel for tips on fishing. Sunday mass was cancelled, so I would watch it on EWTN (Eternal Word Television Network), a Catholic TV and Radio (WQPH 89.3FM) network that I watched or listened to often.

My 59th birthday was on Saturday, April 11, 2020, the day before Easter. So I invited the kids to my apartment to celebrate the event and to make ham and ricotta pie, which is an Ital-ian Easter tradition in our family. In the past, we would always spend Holy Saturday with my side of the family, and Easter Sunday with Dee's side. So it worked out well this year with the same format. The girls gave me everything needed to plant an apartment-sized vegetable garden – seeds for cherry tomatoes, green peppers, and basil, which I planted inside in large pots the following week. A new hobby for me. A home-made birth-day card with drawings of the Easter Bunny was also included. Zach and Emily's gift was a tumbler that reads "Dad," with a bass fish on it. Emily made the stickers on her Cricket sticker machine. They also gave me a card themed on fishing. "Dad, do you want to go trout fishing early tomorrow?" Zach asked excitedly. I was a little reluctant because he was proposing get-ting up before dawn, so we could be at the Squanicook River at dawn. It would be cold. But what the heck, what an opportunity! The night ended with an eclair ring for dessert and a lively card game of Golf. My alarm clock went off at 4:30 a.m. Easter Sun-day, and I dressed warmly for the trip to the Squanicook River in Groton, Massachusetts, which is about a 25-minute drive in

Chapter 15

Zach's truck. We trekked up and down that section of the river in search of the perfect trout honey spot. Finally, we found a small basin, where we could spread out and cast into the water. I was across the basin from Zach and using the fishing pole that he had given me for Christmas and a small tube lure. "Dad, I think I got one!" he exclaimed as he started reeling profusely. I reeled in my line in and hustled over to him, just in time for him to pull in a beautiful 14 inch rainbow trout. He instructed me to cast out and let my lure drag down the current to a spot under a tree that had fallen into the river. "Zach, I think I got one!" My turn to catch another rainbow trout! Zach caught one more, and we packed up for the day after a successful outing. Back at my apartment he taught me how to gut and clean the fish, which we put in the fridge to be cooked up the following week. A little olive oil, butter, and a slice of lemon sealed in tin foil and baked in the oven for about 20 minutes – they were delicious!

George Floyd was murdered on May 25, and the country erupted into violence and chaos as the lockdown from the pandemic continued. What a tragedy. Although watching the video of the George Floyd incident was painful, having it caught on film exposed the reality of how life can be for Blacks in America. Having read Anthony Ray Hinton's book The Sun Does Shine, about his wrongful conviction of two murders in 1985, the 28 years he spent on death row, and his subsequent release in 2015, I wasn't surprised. I know that not all people or police officers in this country are racists, but the minority that are racist still exist. And like mental illness, something has to be done about it.

More fishing, writing, and working out in my apartment.

But no substitute teaching because school was still being taught remotely. Fishing was a good outlet during the pandemic, because you could easily be socially distant and outside, two recommended characteristics of virus control.

June 5 was Gigi's 20th birthday, and she has a new passion for golf, as a beginner. "Dad, take me golfing for my birthday!" So I took her to Butternut Farms Country Club in Stowe, Massachusetts, the day before her birthday. It was a beautiful, sunny Thursday in the mid-80s, nice and dry. We had a 10 a.m. tee time to play nine holes on this 18-hole course, and we were teamed up with two retired gentlemen, George and Pete. With Gigi as a beginner, and me as a hack golfer even though I've been playing for 25 years, these guys were patient with us and more than gracious. I can't remember our scores, but we kept up with them well enough. At the end of the round, George commented to Gigi that she has a nice swing, most likely from all her years in field hockey. I drove her back to the house, and she had a great idea: "Let's go to the beach!" I was reluctant at first because it was after 1 p.m., but I decided, what the heck – it's her birthday, and I don't always get to spend the whole day one-on-one with the kids for their birthdays. So we drove the Milan to Hampton Beach in New Hampshire and parked near the beach. It was slightly overcast when we arrived that afternoon, but we laid out anyways. The water was cold when I went swimming, being early in the season. We couldn't visit the beach without going to a seafood dinner afterwards, so we found an outdoor restaurant nearby. With COVID, New Hampshire was allowing outdoor dining with social distancing and a mask when not at your table. It was a memorable day!

Domenic and Gigi

The divorce negotiations were ongoing, and we finally reached an agreement on the terms. But the courts were closed. Lawyers weren't considered essential personnel unless it was a dire situation, so more hold ups. We finally got our remote court date and, sadly, we were declared divorced on June 9, 2020.

It broke my heart because I still loved her, but it's all for the better, if I'm going to regain control over my life and boost my self-esteem.

EPILOGUE

So What's All this Religion Stuff?

God loves us! He wants a relationship with us, more than he wants souls who follow his commandments out of fear. But he does want us to know and follow His commandments.

The Second Greatest Story Ever Told – Now is the Time of Mercy, by Father Michael Gaitley, MIC, is the story of St. John Paul II and Divine Mercy. "Right now is a time of great grace and mercy for the whole church and the entire world." Published in 2015, in it he explains how St. John Paul II tied together some of the greatest Divine Mercy saints, especially St. Faustina Kowalska (who lived in the 20th century) and sister Margaret Mary (who lived in the 17th century). St. Faustina was born August 25, 1905, in Poland and died October 5, 1938 (Catholic Online). In 1931 Jesus appeared to her to ask that the Divine Mercy image be painted. You see this painting in most Catholic churches today, Jesus holding His left hand over His heart, and his right hand out. Red light gushes forth on His right, downward from His heart, as does pale white light from His left. Under the image are the words "Jesus I Trust in You." The red and white streams from His heart represent the blood and water (baptismal water) that flowed from His heart when the soldier lanced Him on the cross.

Mercy Image

"Now more than ever, is a time of DIVINE mercy," according to St. John Paul II (The Second Greatest Story Ever Told).

A form of Catholicism called Jansenism is the source of our fear, and it reached its highest point in the 17th century. The Second Greatest Story Ever Told calls it a "joyless moral rigorism." It's a heresy – a belief or opinion contrary to orthodox religious (especially Christianity) doctrine (Oxford Dictionary). Catholic guilt is derived from it; you can never measure up.

Unfortunately, Jansenism still reached out into the 20th Century when I was growing up, especially in grammar school at St. Anthony's Parochial School in Fitchburg. The priests and nuns were very strict, which is okay; but they also had a somewhat strict view of religion and of God's relationship with us. When I reverted back to the Catholic Faith in 1995, though, that's the religion that I reverted back to, with a hint of Jansenism. But you rarely get complex subjects the first time around, and especially when you're at a disadvantage to begin with, so my relationship with God had to develop over time. Now I find religion and my relationship with God as a comfort and a guiding principle in my life. Pushed to find a better solution than the materialism and godlessness of modern-day society, my illness was "the wind in my sails" according to my long-time spiritual director, Father Theodore LaPerle.

Why am I Catholic? Before I reverted, I also investigated other forms of spirituality and religion. Witchcraft, or the occult, was the first endeavor, although I didn't realize that palm reading and tarot cards are a form of it. I also investigated Buddhism and other non-Christian religions. I felt comfortable with none of them. Catholicism was destined to be my choice because of the warm and familiar feelings that I had in my extended family growing up, mostly due to my father's mother, Nonna Z, who had all those family gatherings at her house after mass. I felt safe then and needed that safety again in my life. Faith and Family. But, for those who ask the question: why Catholicism? I have three answers unique to the Catholic faith: First – our belief that the Eucharist that we receive every Sunday at mass is the body, blood, soul and divinity of Jesus Christ, so he enters our body and soul. I go to mass to receive the Eucharist every day. Second – confession is the absolute forgiveness of your sins. No matter how serious, as long as you're sorry for your sins (apology) and promise to try not to repeat them, He'll forgive you. That's the mercy Father Gately wrote about. Even if you do repeat them, He'll forgive you over and over if you're trying. Confession prepares us well for the Sacrament of the Eucharist. I go to confession monthly. Third – the rosary is the best spiritual weapon for our times according to Padre Pio.

The rosary is related to our great love for the mother of God, the Blessed Virgin Mary, and we ask her to intercede for us to her Son. I don't understand the Protestant view that Catholics adore and pray to Mary as if she was god. We're only asking the mother of God to intercede to her Son. I pray five decades of the rosary every day.

But I don't overdo religion either. My relationship with God through the Catholic faith is closely matched to my productiveness in the world. But I do pray constantly throughout the day also in an informal way, keeping God at the center of my life. Protestants and all religions are certainly worthy of God's love, and you can find salvation in all of them. I believe that we'll all be judged by Jesus in the end, no matter what our faith is. How other religions enter Heaven is beyond me, but I just know that it's possible. After all, whether we realize it or not, we're all praying to the same God.

What does my faith teach me regarding living everyday life? First – faith in God as a loving Father whose ways are beyond our ways. Faith is believing in him, and trust is that our life is safe in His hands. Second – it taught me about hope. Hope for better days in those times when your life is a burden. Hope for a better future for the world. Hope that one day, we'll be in heaven, our true home. Third – love. Even for our enemies, who many times can teach us a lesson or bring us to a new level of understanding. I recently learned that forgiveness (loving your enemies) is not about becoming a doormat to anyone's desires, but to reach for forgiveness when they do apologize and promise to try not to repeat the same offense. Forgiveness doesn't always mean reconciliation, however. If the person decides that they want to continue to offend you, sometimes you have to avoid them. Forgiveness means praying for blessings for your enemies. I know that's radical. But in all of this, hatred is never an option, because it only burns you up inside, as I witnessed before entering McLean Hospital on that Super Bowl Sunday.

If you're not practicing your faith, join the club. God will always welcome you back. I was away from the faith for over 15 years, from the beginning of college until my nervous breakdown at 34. In the end, God wins. Although He allows evil in the world, "Where evil is found, Grace is ever more present" (Romans 5:20). I've heard that the reason God allows evil in the world is because, if we turn to Him, either it will prevent a greater evil, or it will bring out a greater good. I've experienced this in my life. I'm less fearful of the future, and for bad events in my life, because of it.

Two recent articles in the Boston Herald highlight our need for God again in the world today. The Friday, October 18, 2019, article: "CDC: Youth Suicide Rate Spikes 56 Percent Over Decade," by Rick Sobey, calls out the increase in suicide between the years 2007 and 2017: "The rate of suicide among young people aged 10 to 24 has spiked dramatically over the past decade, according to a new Centers for Disease Control and Prevention report – a disturbing trend, a suicide expert tells the Herald." It continues, "The suicide rate for that age group was stable from 2000 to 2007 but then increased 57 percent between 2007 and 2017, the CDC report states." Later it states "Suicide was the second leading cause of death for people aged 10 to 24 in 2017, behind unintentional accidents. Previously, the second leading cause of death was homicide, which is now third." This article was part of another article in the Herald that day, "Remembering Anna," about the suicide of Anna Aslanian, age 16. Coincidentally, a second totally unrelated article in that same issue: "Share of Americans with no religious affiliations growing," by the Associated Press, states "The portion of Americans with no religious affiliation is rising significantly in tandem with a sharp drop in the percentage that identify as Christian, according to new data from the Pew Research Center. Based on telephone surveys conducted in 2018 and 2019, Pew said Thursday that 65 percent of American adults now describe themselves as Christian, down from 77 percent in 2009. Meanwhile, the portion that describes their religious identity as atheist, agnostic or 'nothing in particular,' now stands at 26 percent, up from 17 percent in 2009." Further on in the article it states, "Pew's data showed a wide gap in terms of religion affiliation – three quarters of Baby Boomers described themselves as Christian, compared to 49 percent of Millennials." The article calls out the challenging times for the Catholic Church and the Southern Baptist Convention due to the clergy abuse scandals. Millennials are aged 22-36 in 2019, not 10-24 like the CDC report studied, but you get the idea; our youth aren't as religious as their parents are. They grew up in the age of the abuse crisis, so who could blame them. Is there a relationship between the spike in the suicide rate and the dramatically lower rate of Christianity among young people of today compared to the Baby Boomers? I argue that there is. We need a better solution than another anti-bullying campaign or 5K walk.

So let's give God another try, no matter what your religion. The world will be a better place because of it!

FINAL WORDS

The Truth Will Set You Free

If you search for the truth, you will find it in the Catholic Church, even today. But it takes a lot of time, effort, and experience—like most other pursuits for excellence. You will also need good, holy priests as spiritual directors and advisors. A few solid friends, and the guts to keep going until you develop a personal relationship with Jesus (and Mary, and Joseph, and the Saints) and learn to be guided by the Holy Spirit.

I believe that one of the problems in the Catholic Church today is that some of the most powerful leaders in recent times haven't promoted the true teachings—Christ in the Eucharist, the power of Confession, The Rosary for healing ourselves, and others (Fatima). Also, we've been taught a lot about God's Justice recently, but very little about His Mercy, which is endless if you ask for it (Divine Mercy). He will forgive you. I believe that horrendous things were allowed to persist for a long time because of this bad element of leadership in the Church, while the good Shepherds were powerless to stop it for whatever reason. Only God knows.

For us to be witnesses of the Truth, living our life with Joy and Confidence will draw the curiosity of anyone who is truly searching for God. If they can reprioritize their life, putting God first, they'll get the desired response from God, even if they make mistakes trying to follow Him. Remember, "Where Evil is found, Grace is Ever more present." (Romans 5:20) Now is a time of Grace for those searching for the Lord, and for those that He is searching for (which is Everyone!!). And God is in control, no matter how bad it looks.

It worked for me, it can work for you...

Keep the Faith,

Domenic - January 17, 2019 - *(the passing of my father, Alfred Orlando Zarrella)*

To find out how to contact Domenic, Bianca, or Dominique, go to our website @**SanitytheBook.com**

BIBLIOGRAPHY

APA.ORG/NEWS/PRESS/RELEASES/2019/05/MENTAL/

HEALTH/SURVEY

Associated Press, "Percentage of Americans with no religious affiliations growing," Boston Herald, October 18, 2019.

Losey, Stephen. https://www.military.com/daily-news/2021/04/05/military-deaths-suicide-jumped-25-end-of-2020.html.

Miller, Matthew. https://blogs.va.gov/VAntage/94358/2021-national-veteran-suicide-prevention-annual-report-shows-decrease-in-veteran-suicides/.

"Remembering Anna." Boston Herald. October 18, 2019.

Sobey, Rick. The Friday, "CDC: Youth Suicide Rate Spikes 56 Percent Over Decade," Boston Herald. October 18, 2019.

Made in United States
North Haven, CT
05 June 2022

19888236R00128